Epley
manœuvre

HIVES AND THE MERLIN

Sir Ian Lloyd and Peter Pugh

ICON BOOKS

Published in the UK in 2004
by Icon Books Ltd., The Old Dairy,
Brook Road, Thriplow, Cambridge SG8 7RG
email: info@iconbooks.co.uk
www.iconbooks.co.uk

Sold in the UK, Europe, South Africa
and Asia by Faber and Faber Ltd.,
3 Queen Square, London WC1N 3AU
or their agents

Distributed in the UK, Europe, South Africa
and Asia by TBS Ltd., Frating Distribution Centre,
Colchester Road, Frating Green, Colchester CO7 7DW

Published in Australia in 2004
by Allen & Unwin Pty. Ltd.,
PO Box 8500, 83 Alexander Street,
Crows Nest, NSW 2065

Distributed in Canada by
Penguin Books Canada,
10 Alcorn Avenue, Suite 300,
Toronto, Ontario M4V 3B2

ISBN 1 84046 644 8

Typesetting by Hands Fotoset

Printed and bound in the UK by Cromwell Press Ltd

CONTENTS

iii

LIST OF ILLUSTRATIONS

Acknowledgements
The photograph of the Merlin-powered Lancaster of RAF Bomber Command flying towards Hitler's Berchtesgaden Chalet is reproduced by kind permission of the Trustees of the Imperial War Museum, London. All the rest are reproduced by kind permission of Rolls-Royce Heritage Trust.

INTRODUCTION

Much has been made of Britain's failure to prepare for war in 1939. Was it the Government's fault or was it the Government responding to the mood of the people? Certainly, Neville Chamberlain seemed popular when he returned from negotiating the Munich Agreement with Adolf Hitler in September 1938. There has been continuous discussion as to whether Chamberlain knew that he had to delay war with Germany, because of Britain's unpreparedness, or whether he genuinely thought Hitler had only limited ambitions and could be appeased.

What is certain is that there were plenty of people telling him in the summer of 1938 that Britain was not ready for war. Sir Thomas Inskip, the Minister for Co-ordination of Defence, told him:

On the question whether we were ready to go to war in a sense this country would never be ready owing to its vulnerable position. With a country as formidable as Germany so close to us we would be bound to go through a period of suffering and serious injury and loss. It was obvious, however, that at the present time we had not reached our maximum preparedness *and should not do so for a year or more*. [authors' italics]

1

Chamberlain flew to see Hitler not once, not twice, but three times in fourteen days in September 1938, the initial trip being his first ever flight. Finally, at the Munich meeting between Hitler, Mussolini, Daladier of France and Chamberlain, Czechoslovakia, without a Czech representative present, was signed over to Germany. Chamberlain flew back to be greeted by large, enthusiastic crowds, first in Downing Street and then in the Mall as he appeared on the balcony of Buckingham Palace with the Royal Family. Many knew that it was a humiliation and a betrayal merely postponing the evil day. As was often the case, Winston Churchill summed up the situation better than most when he said:

The Prime Minister desires to see cordial relations between this country and Germany. There is no difficulty at all in having cordial relations with the German people. Our hearts go out to them. But they have no power ... there can never be friendship between the British democracy and the Nazi Power, that Power which spurns Christian ethics, which cheers its onward course by a barbarous paganism, which vaunts the spirit of aggression and conquest, which derives strength and perverted pleasure from persecution, and uses, as we have seen, with pitiless brutality the threat of murderous force.

That Power cannot ever be the trusted friend of the British democracy.

The die was cast. Hitler's next obvious victim was Poland. Britain and France guaranteed Poland's borders. Hitler, convinced by this time of Britain's unwillingness to fight, invaded Poland on 1 September 1939 and, on 3 September, Chamberlain was forced to broadcast to the nation the spine-chilling words:

This morning the British Ambassador in Berlin handed the German Government a final Note stating that, unless we heard from them by eleven o'clock that they were prepared at once to withdraw their troops from Poland, a state of war would exist between us ... I have to tell you now that no such message has been received and that consequently, this country is at war with Germany.

2

Was Britain unprepared? In many ways, yes. Luckily, so was Germany, especially for a war with islands not connected to Continental Europe. So there was a hiatus, what became known as the Phoney War. The only contact between the fighting forces of Britain and France on the one hand and Germany on the other until summer 1940 was in the air and at sea. This gave Britain especially the chance to step up its arms production and, most significantly, its output of air fighters and bombers and aero engines.

Nevertheless, it was a close-run thing. When the real shooting began in May, with Hitler's successful invasion of Belgium, Holland and France enabling him to contemplate invasion of the British Isles by late summer 1940, it was touch-and-go whether the Royal Air Force would repel the Luftwaffe in what became known as the Battle of Britain.

This book is the story of the engine that powered the fighters that won the Battle of Britain and subsequently powered other fighters and bombers to make certain that Nazi Germany was defeated. It is also the story of the determination and skilful leadership of the man, Ernest, later Lord, Hives, who kept the ever-improving Rolls-Royce Merlin engine rolling off the production line.

Chapter One

Foch Was Right: It Was Only a 20-Year Armistice

Thank Goodness for Rowledge
The Schneider Trophy
'Rigorous Camouflage'
'We Call Her Spitfire'
'The Interceptor Monoplane'

THANK GOODNESS FOR ROWLEDGE

On 11 November 1918, when the Armistice was signed, it was found that it was easier to cease fire than cease production. British industry may have taken a long time to gear up for war production, but by this time it was running at full capacity. Furthermore, in contrast to the mood of autumn 1914 when everyone was saying that the lads would be home by Christmas, in the autumn of 1918 most were expecting the war to continue into 1920 or even 1921. Rolls-Royce continued to manufacture the engines ordered by the Government, but the prospects for further orders seemed dismal, and would depend on the scale of the air force envisaged by Parliament.

The view of the British Government, when peace finally came at the eleventh hour on the eleventh day of the eleventh month in 1918, was that the British Empire would not be involved in another major war for at least ten years, and that they could plan their armed forces on that assumption. Massive reductions in military budgets were made immediately, and wartime air defences abolished.

4

The General Staff have often been accused of short-sightedness in preparations for the Second World War. This is unfair. They knew perfectly well how important bombers and fighters would be, but were expressly forbidden by Government to prepare for such a war.

Nevertheless, the British Government realised that the country must have some sort of air force, and also that a number of aircraft manufacturers would be forced out of business if not given new orders. Partly for this reason of subsidy, and partly to strengthen its hand in international negotiations, the Government set up a Metropolitan Air Force of 23 squadrons in 1922. When the Conservatives replaced the Liberals in power later that year, the number was increased to seventeen fighter and 35 bomber squadrons, with a total of 598 aircraft. In trying to bring some rationalisation to the production of aero engines, Rolls-Royce were chosen as one of the four manufacturers – the others were Bristol, Napier and Armstrong Siddeley – to whom the Government was prepared to give aid after the war.

Just as Rolls-Royce faced competition in the motor car business, they also needed to establish their supremacy in the world of aero engines if they were to stay in the aerospace business. To give some idea of the level of competition, between 1909 and the end of the Second World War, nearly 250 basic types of piston aero engine were built, and in their 900 variants they powered nearly 3,000 different types of aircraft.

In the 1920s, Rolls-Royce found themselves head-to-head in the aero engine field with Napier, their old pre-war rival in the motor car world. In the 32nd Wilbur Wright Memorial Lecture at the beginning of the Second World War, Roy Fedden, chief engineer of the engine department of the Bristol Aircraft Company, said of aero engine development after the First World War:

In Britain, Rolls-Royce who had undoubtedly produced the best engines during the war, although retaining their interest in aero-engine development, again concentrated their main efforts on motor cars. Napier, on the other hand, who had also held a leading position in the motor vehicle world before the war, was the one established concern which took the opposite course, and continued to concentrate on aero-engine work. This decision was influenced, no doubt, by the fact that, at just about the time of the Armistice, they had brought their W.12. liquid-cooled 'Lion' engine of 400 h.p. to a successful state of development, and so had the most advanced British engine of the day. Armstrong Siddeley followed a middle course, and continued with the development of their 14 cylinder two bank radial, concurrently with their motor car work. An exceptional course was taken by the Bristol Company which, although having been concerned only with airframe work, established an aero-engine department to take over the development of the Cosmos Jupiter, which I had had the privilege of initiating with my colleagues at Brazil Strakers during the war. Another factor which influenced the British position was the establishment of the Aircraft Disposal Board with a large stock of engines, which took some years to liquidate, and which undoubtedly had the effect of further depressing interest in new development.

Napier had been given something of a head start by Rolls-Royce in the 1920s, as Rolls-Royce's Managing Director, Claude Johnson, had insisted that the company concentrate its efforts on the development and manufacture of motor cars. Johnson was supported in his views by Ernest Claremont, the Chairman, by his own brother, Basil Johnson, and, to an extent, by Royce himself, who was busy on the 20 hp and Silver Ghost replacement. Only grudgingly was Eric Platford, on his return from helping the would-be conquerors of the Atlantic in Newfoundland in 1919, allowed to spend modest amounts supporting the engines in service with the RAF, foreign air forces and civil airlines. Further design work on aero engines virtually ceased.

At the end of the Second World War, Ernest Hives would say that Rolls-Royce should not make the same mistake it had made after the first war and ignore its aero engine development. However, in 1919 and the early 1920s, contribution to Rolls-Royce's progress on aero engines was confined to overhauls, leaving the field open for Napier's Lion engine, which had been designed by A.J. Rowledge before he left Napier to join Rolls-Royce in 1921 (as assistant chief engineer to Henry Royce). Rowledge's first job at Rolls-Royce was to redesign the Condor, the result being the Condor III engine. He had been asked to reduce the weight of the engine by 600 lbs. He also changed the epicyclic gear to a spur reduction gear, crossbolted the main bearings and introduced marine-type fork and blade connecting rods in place of master and articulated connecting rods. In many ways, the Condor III was a crucial engine. Many of its features were to be retained in the Kestrel, Buzzard, 'R', Merlin and Griffon, including the four-valve head which Royce had introduced on the Condor.

By 1927, Napier were employing 1,600 men and producing about 50 aero engines a month. However, by this time the Lion was reaching its zenith and Napier had failed to come up with a replacement. (They had been greatly disappointed when the Air Ministry decided in 1925 to stop funding development of the Cub engine, which Napier had hoped would replace the Lion.)

Napier and the Lion were not the only competition. From 1922 until 1926, Armstrong Siddeley were the dominant British manufacturer of air-cooled engines. Their Jaguar engine powered the standard post-war fighters – the Grebe, Flycatcher and Siskin. Until 1926, more Jaguars were sold abroad than any other engine. In that year, the engine was overtaken by the simpler and more powerful Bristol Jupiter, and Armstrong Siddeley, in spite of several attempts to win back their superiority, never regained their pre-eminent position as designers of high-power, air-cooled engines.

There were one or two other competitors. Geoffrey de Havilland initially bought surplus engines from the Aircraft Disposals Company and converted them from eight to four cylinders. He then realised that a specially designed light engine could be a viable proposition. The Government did encourage private flying, even if it was not providing funds for the development of engines. De Havilland's Gipsy engine, designed for the Moth and first produced in 1927, was extremely successful. Alvis was also a competitor, though it later undertook Merlin overhauls before becoming a 'sister' firm to Allison for V1710 engines in Britain.

In 1925 Air Chief Marshal Trenchard, after consultation with the Air Ministry, made the decision that all future engines for front-line RAF aircraft should have the capability of being manufactured under licence by firms in the motor car industry. The Air Ministry sent Major G.P. Bulman to the various aero engine manufacturers to tell them of this decision. (Bulman was assistant to Lieutenant-Colonel Fell, the Assistant Director of Technical Development (Engines), who later worked for Rolls-Royce.) Nobody disagreed except Rolls-Royce. Basil Johnson (Claude had just died) told Bulman of the Rolls-Royce tradition of not using licensees. Trenchard was upset, and scrawled across Bulman's report, 'No more Condors'. Rolls-Royce were in danger of being excluded from the aero engine business altogether.

THE SCHNEIDER TROPHY

The Schneider Trophy is a vital part of the Rolls-Royce story. Not only did the engines that Rolls-Royce developed for Supermarine in the late 1920s re-establish the company's reputation as the supreme aero engine maker, but also the work carried out by R.J. (Reginald) Mitchell in designing his S5 and S6 seaplanes led directly to his design of the Spitfire, with all its consequences for Rolls-Royce and the country.

Initially presented by Jacques Schneider, son of a wealthy French arms manufacturer who saw the seaplane as the future of air travel, the rules were simple. The contest must take place over water, the contestants' machines must be sea-worthy, the entries must be sponsored by a governing body (in Britain's case, the Royal Aero Club), and no country could enter more than three contestants. The winning nation would host the contest in the following year, and three consecutive victories would win the Trophy outright. The length would be about 350 kilometres, flown in a number of laps around a closed circuit.

There were two contests before the outbreak of war in 1914. The first, held in Monaco in April 1913, was won by a Frenchman, Maurice Prevost, in a monoplane flying at an average speed of 45.75 mph and powered by a French Gnome rotary engine. The second, in 1914, again in Monaco, was won by an Englishman, Howard Pixton, flying a Sopwith Schneider biplane fitted with floats. His average speed was 86.78 mph, almost twice that of Prevost.

The First World War meant that there was no further contest until 1919, and that proved to be a shambles owing to bad weather, including fog, in Bournemouth Bay, the venue for the contest. The 1920 and 1921 contests were held in Venice. There were no British entries, and both were won by Italy. In 1922 Supermarine entered a modification of the Sea Lion which they had used in 1919, and in a very close contest in the Bay of Naples, brought the Trophy back to Britain. The year 1923 brought entries from the USA, with Lieutenant Rittenhouse winning the Trophy in a Curtiss-CR3.

Mitchell, by this time chief designer of Supermarine, now realised that only a dramatic new design could compete with the Americans. His solution – the S4, a monoplane with a wing of cantilever construction – was so expensive that backing from the Air Ministry was required. Unfortunately, the S4 crashed and the Americans retained the Trophy in 1925 (the 1924 contest had been cancelled). The 1926 race was won again by the Italians with no entry from Britain, but Britain won the Trophy back in 1927 with Mitchell's S5, a greatly improved S4 monoplane.

The year 1928 brought a change in the Schneider Trophy rules. It was agreed that the contest should take place every two years, to give countries more time to develop their machines. The next contest, to be held in England, would now take place in 1929, and Mitchell made one significant change in the aeroplane he designed for this contest. Up to this point, all of his Schneider Trophy entries had been powered by Napier Lion engines, but it was felt by this time that this engine had reached the limit of its development. The only other possible engine supplier was Rolls-Royce.

Major Bulman, for most of the inter-war years the Air Ministry official in charge of aero engine development, wrote later of how Rolls-Royce became involved in the Schneider Trophy:

The third and perhaps greatest problem confronting my early months as A.D.R.D.E. (Assistant Director Research and Development for Engines) related to the Schneider Trophy Race due in September 1929 in England. The engine programme had to be settled early in 1928. Since 1927, Italy had continued to advance rapidly in the Air. The Duce was becoming an increasingly truculent leader adding to the temperature and stress of the international field. The Trophy Race would be the most bitter and significant battle between our two countries.

The stalwart and dependable Lion had won the Race in Venice in 1927 in the Supermarine S.5 with its output of 890 HP for 928 lbs weight, tailored down in most of its external dimensions from the standard Service Lion which had for years given yeoman service in the R.A.F. But had it the prospect of producing a much higher output, some hundreds of HP, entailing undoubtedly the introduction of a supercharger, ground so far untrodden by the Napier team? Would it be justifiable to commit the British effort to this one project?

The alternative was to gamble on a completely new comer in the Rolls-Royce development of the Buzzard, recently typetested for service use at 825 HP for 1,460 lbs weight, supercharged, a bigger brother to the Kestrel but far less established. Indeed it had shown a tendency to crack cylinder heads after only short service, as the Japanese must have found with the trial batch of 100 engines they bought [100 Buzzard engines were built, but only 40 went to Japan], but they remained inscrutable in their silence!

The Rolls-Royce engineers had discussed separately with Reggie Mitchell, the Supermarine designer, and myself, the possibilities latent in this engine, given intensive effort for a short life, and were enthusiastic in their hopes. To Mitchell it would mean a considerable re-hash of his S.5 to accommodate the bigger and heavier engine, with its extra cooling and heavier fuel load. To me it meant a desperate gamble to back something virtually untried, entirely contrary to my habit, and to commit the Air Ministry and the nation

10

to a gigantic bet, instead of playing safe by putting all one's money on the well tried faithful Lion.

Mitchell and I met together alone three times over a short period to resolve the problem, and finally mutually agreed that we should back the Rolls project, largely, and for my part wholly, on the faith I had in the Derby team, A.J. Rowledge, the originator years earlier of the Lion, Elliott, long the right hand of Sir Henry Royce, and Hives, the head of the Experimental Shop at Derby. One felt that their sheer determination and guts would give us the best chance.

I reported Mitchell's and my decision to my chief, Sir John [Josh] Higgins, who immediately asked the Managing Director of R.R. Ltd. to call and settle the deal in principle. Claude Johnson, who had built up the Firm's world wide reputation on Royce's technical brilliance and vision, a man of striking personality, had died in 1926, and his successor [his brother, Basil] it was who came to see Josh and myself, alone. To our utter amazement he begged to be excused from our commission. Racing and all its aspects were things, he said, strictly to be avoided by his firm. Its reputation for sheer quality and perfection must not be smirched by sordid competition of this sort. To participate unwillingly, and quite possibly fail, would be a calamity to the firm with the loss of its prestige, for which the Air Ministry would have to accept grave responsibility. And so on, in dreary defeatism. As I listened to this miserable plea to be 'let off', knowing that the firm's engineers were straining at the leash to go ahead, I uncontrollably blurted out in my fury a single word, unprintable in polite context and essentially masculine. Higgins turned and looked at me for a long second, and then in a steely voice of real Air Marshal calibre said to our guest, 'Mr ...... [Johnson], I order your firm to take on this job. We have complete faith in your technical team. The necessary arrangements will be made between our respective staffs. Good afternoon.' As our disconsolate and vanquished visitor closed the door behind him Josh said to me, 'Thank you for summing up the discussion so succinctly,' and gave a huge chuckle as I shot out of his office to telephone the glad tidings to Rowledge in Derby.

To understand the point that Rolls-Royce had reached in their aero engine development when they were approached by Mitchell in 1928, we have to go back to the early 1920s.

Royce had begun work on a new engine, the FX, later known as the Kestrel, in 1924. The Kestrel's 21.24 litre capacity was similar to the Eagle's 20.32 litres, but they differed in other respects. Initially, the engine had dry steel liners, but problems with cooling soon led to the installation of wet liners in direct contact with the coolant. The FX was a V12 like the Eagle, but instead of each cylinder being separate with its own pressed-steel water jacket, the six cylinders on each bank of the engine were enclosed in a single aluminium casting which served as a common water jacket to that bank. Cylinder heads and gas passages were formed integrally with the cylinder castings. A single overhead camshaft carried on each cylinder block operated the valves, the mechanism, completely enclosed, being lubricated by low-pressure oil. The overall result was a very light and rigid engine. Tested as a direct drive unit in development, in production it was offered in geared form. Initially not supercharged, it subsequently became available in both supercharged and non-supercharged form.

Meanwhile, Richard Fairey had designed and built a bomber called the Fairey Fox, and to power it he imported the successful American Schneider Trophy engine, the Curtiss D12, which was later developed into the Curtiss Conqueror. Powered by the D12, his Fairey Fox bomber was faster than any fighter then in service. Fairey took out a licence to build it in Britain. The Government liked the aeroplane but did not want another aero engine manufacturer, and turned to Royce to see whether he could design an engine better than the Curtiss D12. Rolls-Royce brought a D12 to Derby in 1926 to study it, but this was nearly two years after Royce had started work on the Kestrel; he was not influenced by the Curtiss engine, as has sometimes been alleged.

Many different forms of Kestrel were built. As Alec Lumsden put it in his *British Piston Aero-Engines and their Aircraft*, published by Airlife in 1994:

There can have been few, if any families of engines as complex as the Kestrels, of which 4,750 were built. The variants were very numerous and there has been much uncertainty in the past, as to exactly what Kestrel designations implied. Despite this apparent complication, each variant could be identified by observance of a coded string of letters which logically followed the name and saved a lot of time and space.

And the Kestrel was a critical engine in re-establishing Rolls-Royce's position as the premier supplier of aero engines to the RAF. In the 1920s, as an act of deliberate policy, Rolls-Royce had virtually abandoned aero engine development and production, leaving the field clear to its rivals, especially Napier and Bristol. As Major Bulman put it when writing of the RAF Pageant at Hendon in June 1928:

The four main engine firms were fairly well balanced in the service aircraft then in general use; Siddeleys with their Jaguars in fighters (the Siskin and Grebe) with Bristol catching up in the Bulldog and Hawker Woodcock and also in the larger aircraft, the Sidestrand bomber; Napiers with the Lion maintained the heavy stuff with the Vickers Virginia, the Handley Page Hyderabad bombers and the Fairey IIIF, Rolls with the Condor in the Hawker Horsley.

But the Condor and Hawker Horsley were not going to make Rolls-Royce a serious contender. It was the Kestrel that brought Rolls-Royce back in the 1930s. Ultimately, the Merlin made Rolls-Royce world-famous, but the Kestrel was a very important forerunner. As Harold Nockolds, who wrote *The Magic of a Name* in the late 1930s, made clear:

[T]he fame of the Kestrel does not only rest upon the engines which succeeded it. On its own account it achieved a lasting reputation in the history of aviation, for it was the engine of a classic sequence of R.A.F. machines. It is well to remember that Britain's pilots at the outbreak of the Second World War – especially the fighter pilots – largely owed their fitness for the coming struggle for supremacy in the air to the fact that they had been brought up on the Kestrel breed of aircraft. Their early flying had been done on Hawker Harts and Furies and Fairey Fireflies before those magnificent biplanes were supplanted by Hurricanes and later by Spitfires. But the Kestrel outlived those early first-line fighters, and as the engine of the Miles Master it continued to help in the advanced training of new recruits to the ranks of fighter pilots for some time after the war had started.

Even before the FX was named the Kestrel, Royce had identified the need for a more powerful engine. Using the same basic design as the 'F' engine, the 'H' engine was produced with 70 per cent greater cubic capacity. (Much of the work was done by R.W.H. Bailey, who added extra features such as saddle studs.) It was test run in June 1928, and Royce himself was so pleased with the speed of the development of the 'H' engine that on 13 June 1928 he sent this telegram:

WORMALD, BAILEY, ROYCAR DERBY. EXTREMELY PLEASED WITH EXCELLENT WORK DONE INTRODUCING LARGER AERO ENGINE SO QUICKLY THANKS TO YOUR EFFORTS AND THOSE ASSISTING. ROYCE.

Such open praise from the boss was rare indeed!

This was the point that Rolls-Royce aero engine development had reached when Mitchell approached them to inquire about an engine to challenge for the Schneider Trophy. Royce initially looked at a narrow-angle V16 but decided, with the limited time available, that he had only one option. That was to take the most powerful engine available, the Buzzard (still called the 'H' engine at that stage), and soup it up to create the 'Racing H', or more briefly in due course, simply the 'R' engine.

Rod Banks of the Ethyl Corporation, who had already established himself as one of the country's experts on motoring and aircraft fuel, wrote in his book *I Kept no Diary*:

Hives, Rowledge and A.C. Lovesey went down to see Royce at his home and head-quarters at West Wittering in October 1928 and found him enthusiastic. It was a bright autumn morning and Royce suggested a stroll along the beach; as they walked he pointed out the local places of interest. But Royce, who walked with a stick, was a semi-invalid, as Montagu Napier had been, and he soon tired. 'Let's find a sheltered spot,' he said, 'and have a talk.'

Seated on the sand dunes against a groyne, Royce sketched the rough outline of a racing engine in the sand with his stick. Each man was asked his opinion in turn, the sand was raked over and adjustments made. The key to the engine was simplicity. 'I invent nothing,' was Royce's philosophy, 'inventors go broke.' Like the Kestrel and the Buzzard the new engine would have only 12 cylinders, against the 18 of the Isotta-Fraschini and the 24 of the Packard. The bore and stroke would be 6" by 6.6", and the compression ratio 6:1. The secret of increased power would lie in supercharging.

And, as we have seen, the company had effectively received an order from the Air Ministry to develop an engine capable of winning the Schneider Trophy and putting the upstart Mussolini in his place.

Hives had never been in favour of neglecting the aero engine side of the business, and it was largely through his influence that the engineers Cyril Lovesey, A.A. Rubbra and Ray Dorey had been recruited to work specifically on aero engines.

Rowledge had already persuaded Rolls-Royce to take on the expert on supercharging, James Ellor, who had worked at the Royal Aircraft Establishment (RAE). Ellor was being tempted to take his skills to the USA, and the Air Ministry could not match the offer within Civil Service pay scales. To keep Ellor in Britain, it was agreed that Rolls-Royce should make him an offer.

The power of an engine depends on the mass of air and fuel it can consume in a given time, and a supercharger provides a means of getting air through an engine of given size and capacity. Ellor had introduced supercharging into the Kestrel and Buzzard engines, but principally to restore power at altitude. On the 'R' engine, the intent was to increase power at low altitude. His design for this engine included a forward-facing air intake which converted forward airspeed energy into pressure energy, a unique development at that time.

Royce had allowed the design to be handled in Derby though, of course, the design details were still subject to his personal supervision. There were now ten in the aero engine team in Derby, rather than two as in the early 1920s, and they worked day and night. As a result, the engine was completed and tested successfully within three months.

The S6 was similar to the S5, but larger to accommodate the new engine. Fuel consumption was greater, and the floats were redesigned to act as fuel tanks. On its trial run, the pilot, Squadron Leader A.H. Orlebar (Orlie), found he could not get the S6 off the water as, at each attempt, the seaplane swung violently to port due to torque from the propeller. Mitchell solved this problem by transferring most of the fuel to the starboard float. After some hair-raising moments, the S6 won the Trophy for Britain in 1929 and Rolls-Royce, Supermarine and the fuel and oil companies made the most of the favourable publicity. Rolls-Royce were so grateful to Mitchell that they presented him with a Rolls-Royce car.

Britain had now won the Schneider Trophy twice in succession. A third victory in 1931 would win it outright.

As Mitchell made modifications to the S6, Rolls-Royce managed to improve the 'R' engine to give an output of 2,350 hp, primarily by making the crankshaft and centrifugal blower run faster, and by increasing the air intake. Their biggest problem was the extra heat produced by the more powerful engine. Somehow they needed to dissipate some 40,000 BTUs of heat per minute. To dissipate this heat from the exhaust valve heads, they introduced sodium-cooled valves. The sodium-cooled valve technology came from the Williams Rich Corporation in the USA; Rolls-Royce therefore had to take out a sub-licence from the Bristol Aircraft Company, because all components had to be manufactured in the competitor nation. The length of the floats was increased, not only to provide more cooling surfaces but also to hold more fuel. Other modifications were made to the intricate oil cooling system.

All parts of the engine needed to be strengthened to take the stress of the higher power output. The engineers set themselves the target of a 60-minute run at full throttle. As testing continued day and night throughout the spring of 1931, the citizens of Derby protested. Rolls-Royce needed the help of the mayor to appeal to their patriotism at the expense of their sleep. On 12 August, with a month to go, the engine passed the test, running for a full hour at 3,200 rpm and giving 2,350 hp.

Gordon Mitchell knew the debt of gratitude his father felt for Rolls-Royce:

The vital part played by Rolls-Royce, led by their Experimental Manager, Ernest (later Lord) Hives, in the successful outcome of the 1931 race, cannot be overemphasised and Mitchell was only too ready to acknowledge their outstanding contribution.

What were the lasting benefits to the development of aero engines of the Schneider Trophy? Arthur Rubbra, who joined the Rolls-Royce Experimental Department in 1925, became chief designer in 1940 and technical director in 1954, said:

I think there are a number of areas where the development of the Merlin was helped by the work done on the R engine, although the target of completion of an hour's run in one piece at full output was rather different from that of completing the official service type test. For this reason, the satisfactory solution of such troubles by this method does not always read across to those met with in service life.

However, there is no doubt that such running at high output for short duration does help considerably in pin-pointing quickly the likely trouble spots and was used extensively and successfully as a general test procedure in the development of the Merlin.

R.J. Mitchell himself produced an article which was published in *Aeronautical Engineering* on 25 December 1929 in which he made it clear that, in his view, information and experience gained in the development of racing aircraft had a profound influence on the design of both civil and military aircraft. He wrote:

During the last 10 years there has been an almost constant increase in speed in our racing types. To maintain this steady increase very definite progress has been essential year by year. It has been necessary to increase the aerodynamic efficiency and power-to-weight ratios of our machines; to reduce the consumption and frontal area of our engines; to devise new methods of construction; and to develop the use of new materials. The results obtained in the form of speed have been a direct and absolute indication of our progress in aeronautical development.

Sir George Edwards, who succeeded Rex Pierson as chief designer at Vickers and rose in the aircraft industry to become Chairman and Managing Director of the British Aircraft Corporation, wrote:

There can be no doubt that the boldness of these designs and the passion for engineering detail which they displayed made a profound impact on aeronautical design and set the scene for the successful generation of British fighters which were so decisive in saving Britain from defeat in later years. If the industry had been limited during these inter-war years to design studies alone and had not been able to translate ideas into hardware by actually building aeroplanes, it is certain that such successful fighters as the Spitfire and the Hurricane would not have emerged.

From Rolls-Royce's point of view, the performance of the 'R' engine in the Schneider Trophy proved to be a turning-point in its progress as an aero engine manufacturer. This is how Alec Harvey-Bailey (the son of R.W.H. Bailey, one of Royce's earliest and most able engineers) put it:

To look back a little, although Rolls-Royce had developed an enviable reputation in the aero engine field by 1918 and had subsequently powered the great pioneering flights, including the start of civil aviation, the 1920s saw the Company slip into third place behind Bristol and Napier. At the end of the twenties it was the performance of the R type racing engine which overshadowed the competition, both British and foreign, in the Schneider Trophy races and put Rolls-Royce into serious contention for major RAF contracts.

And to put the final seal on the beneficial publicity from the winning of the Schneider Trophy, Hives was determined that the S6B should achieve a new World Absolute Air Speed Record. Orlebar had achieved it in the S6 after the 1929 contest, attaining a speed of 357 mph. Since then the record had been raised to 379 mph, but the target now was 400 mph. Hives wrote in memos at the time that '400 miles per hour' was a headline maker. The Air Ministry, not interested in such frivolities, wanted the High Speed Flight to hand the Calshot base back to the Flying Boat Squadron. According to Rod Banks, 'This caused a furore, but the decision was reversed after Sir Henry Royce interceded on behalf of the High Speed Flight.'

Hives asked Banks if more power could be attained by altering the fuel. Certainly there was no time to modify the engine greatly. With Ray Dorey, Banks mixed a high-alcohol-content fuel cocktail which gave an extra 250 bhp. The final mix was 60 per cent methanol, 30 per cent benzole and 10 per cent acetone, plus lead. This was fine for performance, but it meant that some modifications to the engine were needed, and it also caused problems with the tanks – the concoction proved to be a good solvent of paint and the sealing compounds. Finally, all was ready and, as Banks put it:

[Flight Lieutenant George Stainforth] then opened the throttle and fairly shot off the lighter for the take-off. On reaching the end of each run on the speed course, he throttled back somewhat on the turn towards the next run and wet fuel vapour was seen coming from the exhausts! But the magic figure was surpassed by 7.5 mph.

'RIGOROUS CAMOUFLAGE'

In spite of the mood of pacifism that permeated the country in the early 1930s a few more knowledgeable, some would say realistic, people were determined that Britain should re-arm to be ready for what they felt would be another European, if not World, war in the foreseeable future.

Sholto Douglas, who became Commander-in-Chief of Fighter Command during the Second World War and later Marshal of the Royal Air Force, wrote in his book *Years of Command*, published by Collins in 1966:

Those of us who had access to the best that our intelligence had to offer could not help but be aware of what was going on in Germany in the build-up of their armed forces. We had known for a long time that the Germans had been sending experienced pilots to Russia to keep up their training in military aviation. The story of the way in which these developments went even further has since been placed freely on record by Adolf Galland, who was to become one of the foremost German fighter pilots of the Second World War. He has spoken of a talk that he had with Hermann Goering in the Spring of 1933. 'The secret training of German pilots in Russia, used as a temporary expedient, must now come to an end', Goering told him. To that Galland added: '… we now had the opportunity of training our fighter pilots with the Italian Air Force. In order to avoid international complications for Italy as well as for Germany, the whole affair had to be treated with the greatest possible secrecy and carried out under rigorous camouflage.'

Intelligence about German activities was brought back by a number of visitors, among them Mutt Summers, the Vickers chief test pilot. Summers had the ear of the Vickers Chairman, Sir Robert McLean, who pressed the Government to sanction the building of a modern fighter aircraft. Unfortunately, allied to the pacifist approach and the reluctance to raise the necessary public expenditure was a widespread belief that 'the bomber will always get through', and that therefore fighters were a waste of time. Fortunately, Air Marshal Sir Hugh Dowding, then Air Member for Supply and Research, did not believe in this theory. He wanted to build a powerful fighter force, which he saw as essential for the defence of the country. In 1930 the Air Ministry issued Specification F. 7/30, a blueprint for the fighter that Dowding thought necessary for such a defence.

The specification required a day and night fighter to replace the obsolete fighter then in service with the RAF. Essential requirements were stipulated as:

- low landing speed and short landing run
- maximum speed of 250 mph

- steep initial climb rate for interception
- high manoeuvrability
- good all-round view.

While no shape of air frame was specified, the fighter was to be armed with four Vickers machine guns.

Many manufacturers built prototypes in response to Specification F. 7/30, most of them powered by the Rolls-Royce Goshawk engine. However, Sir Robert McLean was very keen that Supermarine should win the contract, and asked Mitchell and his team to proceed with a design suggestion with all possible speed. Their first attempt, the Type 224, powered by a 600 hp Rolls-Royce Goshawk II engine, a derivative of the Kestrel but with evaporative water cooling, was a failure and the Government awarded a contract for the production of the Gloster Gladiator biplane.

In designing Type 224 as a monoplane construction, Mitchell was breaking away from the accepted standard of the time. The classic fighter throughout the world at the beginning of the 1930s was a biplane with either a radial or an inline engine, a fixed undercarriage, an open cockpit and two rifle-calibre machine guns. Its top speed was no more than 200 mph and its range was about 250 miles.

Even as late as 6 July 1935, when King George V reviewed 37 squadrons (consisting of 356 aircraft of the RAF) at Mildenhall and Duxford, every single aeroplane on view was a biplane. In squadron service, the fastest fighter was the Gloster Gauntlet, capable of just over 200 mph and armed, like its 1917–18 predecessors, merely with twin machine guns. Three squadrons were flying the Hawker Fury 1; the rest flew the obsolescent Bristol Bulldog. The bomber units were all biplanes, none of which could reach 200 mph.

In the USA the Curtiss and Boeing fighters and in Britain the Bristol Bulldog and Hawker Fury all conformed to standard biplane design. However, various designers were testing monoplanes. The French were looking at parasol designs with the single wing above the fuselage on struts, while the Italians favoured the Warren truss, a system of V-shaped struts.

21

Junkers, the German manufacturer, had produced mono-planes as far back as the First World War. But these were exceptions. The norm was still the biplane.

The British Government tried to persuade Vickers to switch the engine on Type 224 from the Goshawk to the Napier Dagger, but Vickers resisted. Disillusioned with the Government, McLean became convinced that the specification laid down was not good enough. In a letter to *The Sunday Times* in August 1957 he wrote:

I felt that they [the design team] would do much better by devoting their qualities not to the official experimental fighter but to a real killer fighter. After unfruitful discussions with the Air Ministry, my opposite number in Rolls-Royce, the late A.F. Sidgreaves, and I decided that the two companies together should themselves finance the building of such an aircraft.

The Air Ministry was informed of this decision, and was told that in no circumstances would any technical member of the Air Ministry be consulted or allowed to interfere with the design.

Within a month, on 1 December 1934, the Air Ministry responded to this no-nonsense approach by issuing a contract for £10,000 (about £500,000 today) for the development of the new 'killer' fighter. Rolls-Royce also contributed £7,500. Mitchell now made several radical changes to the design of Type 224. After long discussions with his Canadian aero-dynamicist, Beverley Shenstone, he abandoned the straight-winged design for the now famous elliptical configuration. The wing was also made as thin as possible, though near its root it had to be thick enough to take the retractable under-carriage. The cockpit was given a sliding canopy to reduce drag. Most importantly, the steam-cooled Goshawk engine was replaced by the new Rolls-Royce PV12 engine (see below).

Rolls-Royce were as aware as anyone of the need for new fighters with greater power. Virtually every British aircraft was a fabric-covered biplane with so many struts and wires that it was impossible to improve performance by more than a fraction. Cyril Lovesey suggested that the firm should buy the latest and most streamlined monoplane available, and the choice of the German Heinkel HE70 was made. A Kestrel engine was shipped to Rostock, and while it was waiting for the Heinkel to be modified to accommodate it, the Kestrel was used in the maiden flights of two of Germany's most important aircraft of the Second World War: the Junkers JU 87 'Stuka' and the Messerschmitt Bf 109. Once in the Heinkel, it showed the potential of monoplanes over biplanes, reaching 260 mph with six people on board.

Sir Henry Royce knew it was vital that, with or without Government help, a new engine should be developed. One of his last decisions, in October 1932, was to authorise the development of a new engine, bigger than the Kestrel but smaller than the Buzzard, and incorporating as much 'R' technology as possible. It was called the PV12 (Private Venture 12-cylinder). This was a courageous decision, because the company's level of output of aero engines had been extremely low in the 1920s, and remained so into the early 1930s. In 1928 Rolls-Royce produced only 67 aero engines out of a total UK output of 539, in 1929 its share was down to 35 out of 721, in 1930 it was 122 out of 726, and in both 1931 and 1932 it was still only 315 out of 637 and 738 respectively.

As Gordon Mitchell said in his book:

The decision to fit the Merlin engine [developed from the PV12] into Mitchell's Type 300 fighter was a vital turning point in the development of the Spitfire.

The Kestrel had proved to be a great success in the Hawker Fury, and the Merlin took the concept a stage further. As the following memo from Hives to his managing director, Arthur Sidgreaves, on 4 November 1936 makes clear, experience on the Kestrel was invaluable when it came to developing the Merlin.

The following are a few notes which we wish to discuss at the lunch on Friday.

MERLIN POSITION

The Merlin engine, except for the cylinders and valves, has now reached a stage when in spite of the extra power it has a degree of reliability greater than the Kestrel. ...

At present we have a release for 100 Merlin Fs. Although at the present time we have started on the jigs and tools for the 'G' type cylinders, we must have release for the first Contract of 190 Merlin engines to all be the 'F' type. We cannot possibly deliver any engines with the 'G' type until next April. We are faced with the position in the factory that the Kestrel machine is running out, and we must start on the Merlin engines in order to keep our men together.

When the PV12 was initially built, the 'A' and 'B' Merlins had combined cylinder blocks and crankcases, and a Kestrel-type bathtub head. Single-cylinder testing with a ramphead showed some performance benefits, and the 'C' Merlin was effectively a 'B' Merlin with a ramphead. This engine flew in the prototype Hurricane and Spitfire. The 'C' Merlin also had a separate block, and therefore a two-piece block with a ramphead. The Merlin 'F' retained the two-piece block with ramphead, and went into production as the Merlin I, which was installed in the Fairey Battle.

The ramphead did not give the anticipated performance benefits, and also gave cracking problems. Rolls-Royce recognised that going back to a single, Kestrel-type block would at least be going back to the devil they knew. They reverted to it in the Merlin II, which went into Hurricanes and Spitfires. It was introduced on the Merlin 22, and was standard on all marks of the engine introduced thereafter.

This is what Arthur Rubbra – placed by many alongside Royce, Rowledge and Elliott as one of Rolls-Royce's greatest engineers – said of the early development of the Merlin:

In the early 1930s it became evident that a larger engine than the Kestrel would be required. It was called PV12 with a bore and stroke of 5.4×6in, initially giving around 750 hp. It was developed into the 1,000 hp Merlin. In order to provide a more rigid engine crankcase, to allow for higher crankshaft speeds, it was decided to cast the cylinder jacket portion of the cylinder block in one piece with the crankcase and to provide a separate cylinder head with the cylinder liner joint flange clamped between it and the crankcase. This presented quite a foundry problem in maintaining sectional thickness throughout, but this was solved in due course. It was soon discovered, however, on development that a major difficulty was presented because failures in the reciprocating components usually resulted in serious damage to the large crankcase-cum-cylinder jacket casting, this proving an expensive replacement and time-consuming job. Moreover, it was considered that once the separate jacket was bolted to the crankcase the final result, as regards the rigidity of the assembly, was very little different from the one-piece casting and the weight saving achieved by the latter was also small, so the principle of the one-piece crankcase and jacket was abandoned and never raised again. It was, however, used successfully on the V12 engine of the Phantom III motor car.

Elliott carried out a redesign, reverting from the original double helical reduction gear of the PV12 to detachable cylinder blocks and a spur reduction gear. His engine retained the 5.4 inch bore and 6 inch stroke with 1,650 cubic inch (27 litre) capacity. Elliott made a significant change in cylinder design, adopting (after single-cylinder tests) a ramp or semi-penthouse combustion chamber. He had designed this as a two-piece block to try to eliminate the internal coolant leaks to which the Kestrel was prone. The ramphead had shown great promise on single-cylinder tests, and was promoted by a brilliant young graduate, J.D. Pearson, who ultimately became Chairman of the company. But when it was used on the full engine it did not give the anticipated performance, and its asymmetric shape led to cracking in service use. At this point, Hives stepped in and made the decision to revert to a Kestrel-type one-piece block with a single-plane combustion chamber for immediate production, while sanctioning the design of a two-piece block which would eliminate the occasional coolant leakage problem and later facilitate significant power increases.

One initial design idea, as early as 1933, had been for an 'upside down' engine, because in this position the wide 'V' of

25

the banks of cylinders would not hamper the pilot's vision, and the exhaust pipes would be below the fuselage, improving the cooling. And indeed, at the end of the First World War Royce had looked at the possibility of designing an inverted Eagle engine. However, both Rolls-Royce and the aircraft manufacturers Hawker and Supermarine quickly decided that the disadvantages of such a design outweighed the advantages, and the concept was abandoned.

According to Harold Nockolds, a mock-up of the 'upside down' engine was made, and was seen on the floor of Rowledge's office by a party of German aeronautical engineers on an official visit to Derby. Nockolds goes on to say:

The Germans evidently thought they had noticed something of supreme significance. There is every reason to believe that the design of the inverted Daimler-Benz engine used in the Messerschmitt 109 and the Junkers engine sprang from this visit to Derby. From their point of view, the inverted engine was desirable because it enabled them to fire the cannon through the airscrew shaft, but this had the serious result of forcing them to mount the supercharger on the side of the engine instead of at the end, a position which necessitated complex piping and which made it difficult to find a suitable place for carburettors. The Germans' later preference for direct fuel injection was attributable to the difficulty of carburettor layout, and not to any objection to carburettors as such.

As we shall see, direct fuel injection gave the Germans a distinct advantage in the dive in the initial stages of the war, until the British modified their carburettors. Whether this surmise by Nockolds is accurate we shall perhaps never know, but as his book was effectively an official history of the company, the Rolls-Royce directors clearly believed it to be the case.

'WE CALL HER SPITFIRE'

By early 1936, the prototype Spitfire, with the serial number K5054, was ready for its first flight. Sir Robert McLean insisted on the name Spitfire, though others at Supermarine, including Mitchell, were not so keen. McLean had become keen on the name 'Spitfire' because it had been suggested by his effervescent daughter, Annie.

She had returned home early one morning from an all-night party to find her father discussing the new fighter with his Vickers colleagues and Reginald Mitchell, Jeffrey Quill and Mutt Summers. They were struggling to find a name and Annie began to laugh at them. Sir Robert told her to b....r off to bed, which she did but as she went up the stairs she called back, 'You men are hopeless, why don't you call it after me?'

All except Sir Robert looked puzzled but he said, 'Yes, perfect!'

One of the others queried, 'Perfect, how come?'

'We call her Spitfire.'

The earlier failure, Type 224, had also been called Spitfire. On 5 March, according to Mutt Summers's log book, but almost certainly on 6 March from the evidence of test pilot Jeffrey Quill's record, Mutt Summers took K5054, the Spitfire, on its first test flight.

The aeroplane (F37/34 Type 300) was still unnamed, and was referred to simply as 'the Fighter'. It was unpainted and still in its works finish, with protective treatment on its metal surfaces, and its engine cowlings in natural but unpolished duralumin finish. For the first flight, a special fine pitch wooden propeller was fitted, in order to give higher rpm for take-off and to minimise the effect of torque reaction. Jeffrey Quill, one of the great test pilots of this era, wrote in his book *Spitfire, A Test Pilot's Story*:

There was a light wind blowing across the aerodrome which meant that Mutt had to take the short run and he taxied towards one of the four large Chance lights which (in those days) were situated round the perimeter, turned into wind and opened the throttle. The aeroplane was airborne after a very short run and climbed away comfortably. Mutt did not retract the under-carriage on that first flight – deliberately, of course – but cruised fairly gently around for some minutes, checked the lowering of the flaps and the slow flying

27

and stalling characteristics, and then brought K5054 in to land. Although he had less room than he would probably have liked, he put the aeroplane down on three points without too much 'float', in which he was certainly aided by the fine pitch setting of the propeller. He taxied towards the hangar and the point where we in the group of Supermarine spectators were standing. This included R.J. Mitchell, Alan Clifton, Beverley Shenstone, Alf Faddy, Ernest Mansbridge, 'Agony' Payn, Stuart Scott-Hall and Ken Scales, the foreman in charge of the aeroplane. There must also have been quite a few other people there but there certainly was not a crowd. It was very much a Supermarine 'family affair'.

When Mutt shut down the engine and everybody crowded round the cockpit, with R.J. foremost, Mutt pulled off his helmet and said firmly, 'I don't want anything touched.' This was destined to become a widely misinterpreted remark. What he meant was that there were no snags which required correction or adjustment before he flew the aircraft again. The remark has crept into folklore implying that the aeroplane was perfect in every respect from the moment of its first flight, an obviously absurd and impracticable idea. After the 15-minute first flight the aircraft was still largely untested and unproven, having done one take-off and one landing. Mutt was far too experienced a hand to make any such sweeping statement at that stage in the game.

However, it was a highly successful and encouraging first flight and Mutt Summers, with his experience of flying a great variety of prototype aircraft, was a highly shrewd judge of an aeroplane. By now I knew him well enough to see that he was obviously elated. Certainly to those of us watching from the ground 'the Fighter' in the air took on a very thoroughbred and elegant appearance, a strong but indefinable characteristic which was to remain with it through-out its long, varied and brilliantly successful life as a fighting aeroplane. Later that afternoon I flew Mutt back to Brooklands in the Falcon and we put the aircraft away and walked across to have a drink in Bob Lambert's well-known and congenial Brooklands Flying Club bar. Mutt was pleased, obviously, to have one more successful first flight tucked under his belt [apart from professional pride, the test pilot who flew a maiden flight received a substantial bonus], and I felt excited about this long, sleek and elegant machine which I knew that soon I would fly. A hundred yards from where Mutt and I were leaning against the bar was the hangar in which was standing K5083, the prototype Hurricane, which had made its first flight in the hands of George Bulman some four months previously.

So the two new fighter aircraft – destined four years later to save our country in time of war – had now both flown in prototype form. Neither was yet anywhere near being a practical fighting machine nor was either yet ordered in quantity by the Royal Air Force, so much work still remained to be done. Ironically perhaps, the very next day, 7 March, Hitler's troops re-entered the demilitarised zone of the Rhineland in direct defiance of the Versailles Treaty.

On 26 May 1936, Humphrey (later Air Marshal Sir Humphrey) Edwardes Jones tested the Spitfire at Martlesham Heath on behalf of the Air Ministry. On the strength of his report to Sir Wilfrid Freeman, and figures supplied by Supermarine, the Air Ministry placed an order for 310 Spitfires on 3 June. (A contract for 600 Hurricanes from Hawker was signed on the same day.)

Unfortunately, the production of the 310 Spitfires was to prove enormously difficult for Supermarine. Mitchell's Spitfire was revolutionary, and almost every feature called for new and complex manufacturing techniques. The fuselage was to be made in three sections: a tubular case for the engine, a monocoque centre and a detachable aft.

The spars on which the wings were built were made up of tubes that fitted one inside the other. Each tube was different in length so that the spar was thickest where most strength was needed, at the root of the wing, and hollow at the tip. The leading edge of the wing was covered with heavy gauge metal that gave the wing immense strength, while aft of the spar it was clad in aluminium sheeting of a lesser gauge. This gave an ideal combination of lightness and strength.

'THE INTERCEPTOR MONOPLANE'

Alongside the Spitfire in the Battle of Britain was the Hawker Hurricane. Indeed, there were more Hurricanes than Spitfires in Fighter Command at that time. The Spitfire, generally accepted as a more effective fighter, has tended to win more of the accolades but, as Jeffrey Quill pointed out in his book *Spitfire, A Test Pilot's Story*, the Spitfire was not favoured by the Air Ministry until it had proved itself in battle.

Recognising the essential strengths of Mitchell's design, Smith [successor to Mitchell at Supermarine] set about the task of expanding its capabilities and performance to the maximum. He recognised and exploited the whole area of advancing technologies within the industry, more especially the potential power growth of the Merlin and Griffon engines, and the advances in aircraft ancillary equipment. 'If Mitchell was born to design the Spitfire,' wrote J.D. Scott, 'Joe Smith was born to defend and develop it.' The verb 'to defend' perhaps needs some explanation. Although much liked by pilots from the outset the Spitfire never found much real favour with the Air Council until it had decisively proved its mettle in battle over Dunkirk. Originally many technical people were suspicious of it, many production advisers in the Air Ministry did not care for it, and the Air Council were outraged during the latter part of 1937 and during 1938 by the delays in production.

On 7 June 1939 a memorandum was sent to the Chief of the Air Staff by the Air Member for Development and Production (AMDP), Sir Wilfrid Freeman, in which he referred to 'orders to be placed now with certain firms whose existing orders will run out early in 1940'. On the subject of Supermarine he wrote: 'Supermarine will run out of their order for Spitfires in February or March 1940 and since it will be impossible to get a new aircraft into production at Supermarine before September 1940 there is certain to be a six-month gap which we will have to fill.

'In order to be able to bridge the gap with as few machines as possible, Supermarine will be told later on to reduce the amount of sub-contracting and get their men onto single shift, so that although Supermarine production is likely towards the end of the present contract to exceed 48 aircraft per month it is hoped that we can reduce the gap production to 30 aircraft a month.'

He went on: 'Vickers are pressing for a more generous release of Spitfires for foreign orders, and it seems to me that provided no releases are made until October, we could go some way to meet them this year and could release aircraft for foreign orders freely after the spring of next year, when the Castle Bromwich factory will be coming into production.' Later in the same memorandum he wrote: 'The type of aircraft that could be put into production at Supermarine after the end of their contract would be Beau-fighter, Gloster Fighter, Lysander or Westland (F. 37/35).'

Clearly, the Air Ministry felt that the initial order for 310 Spitfires might be the total ever made. As we know now, the eventual total was about 23,000.

Part of the reason why many in the Air Ministry and the RAF saw little need for the Spitfire if the Hurricane was going to be much easier to produce stemmed from the view that the main purpose of such fighters would be to attack bombers. They thought that fighter-to-fighter combat was a relic of the First World War, when aircraft were much slower and could hold each other in their sights long enough for a two-second burst of fire. They viewed both the Spitfire and the Hurricane as bomber destroyers, and the Boulton Paul Defiant was thought of in the same way. As it turned out, the battle over France and the Battle of Britain showed that all three could cope with bombers, but only the Spitfire and Hurricane could mix it with German fighters. Ultimately, only the Spitfire was a true match for the best of the Luftwaffe.

The Hurricane, on the other hand, was relatively straightforward to produce, and on those grounds alone it was looked on with favour by the Air Ministry. It also had some advantages over the Spitfire. For example, it was a more stable gun platform. Its gunfire converged more effectively since it flew absolutely straight, whereas the Spitfire tended to snake around. It was easier to take off the ground and to land, and it could absorb enormous punishment.

Harry Hawker, with Mackenzie-Grieve, had taken part in the race to be the first to make a non-stop Atlantic flight, and indeed they were ahead of Alcock and Brown, when they were forced down into the Atlantic in May 1919. Hawker survived this accident but was killed shortly afterwards testing his

Nieuport Goshawk entry at Hendon. His company survived and in 1923 Sydney (later Sir Sydney) Camm joined as senior draughtsman. Though Camm lacked academic qualifications, Sopwith, the Managing Director, soon realised that his practical experience gained at Martinsydes between 1912 and 1921 was of great value, and he appointed him chief designer in 1925. It was a brilliant decision. From Camm's drawing board came all of the Hart variants – the Fury, Super Fury, Osprey, Audax and (for South Africa) the Hartebeeste – followed by the Hurricane, Typhoon and Tempest, and the Centaurus-powered Fury and Sea Fury. When the jet age arrived, there came the Sea Hawk, Hunter, Harrier and Hawk.

By the end of the 1920s, Camm was realising that the biplane was reaching the maximum of its fighter potential, and that its performance could not be much improved. (In the air exercises of 1930, no fighter managed to catch his own light bomber, the Hart – powered, of course, by a Rolls-Royce Kestrel.) In the early 1930s, as Reg Mitchell was working on his monoplane ideas at Supermarine, Camm began to work on his idea of a Fury monoplane. The Air Ministry, still remembering the disintegration of two monoplanes in 1912, was still largely against the type, but Germany's withdrawal from the Disarmament Conference and the League of Nations concentrated at least some minds on the need for faster fighters.

Nevertheless, no Government funding was initially forthcoming, and just as Rolls-Royce were to develop their PV (Private Venture) 12, the Merlin, Hawker were forced to fund development of the monoplane Fury. The Merlin replaced the Goshawk in Camm's design, which necessitated changes, but the steel tubular structure, fabric covering and overall strength which had been a feature of Camm's designs all remained. New features included a 'greenhouse' built around the pilot because of the anticipated faster speed. Leading and trailing edges of the wings were slightly tapered, and a large radiator was situated under their centre.

The undercarriage was still fixed as in the Fury biplane, and the armament was restricted to four machine guns. Camm moved the radiator eighteen inches aft because the Merlin was heavier than the Goshawk, and this made room for a retractable undercarriage. After discussions with a young squadron leader in the Operational Requirements Branch of the Air Ministry, Ralph Sorley (later Air Marshal Sir Ralph Sorley KCB OBE DSO DFC), who was convinced that monoplane fighters would fly at speeds enabling pilots to hold the target in their sights for no more than two seconds, Camm designed eight guns into his wings.

As the 1930s wore on, the Air Ministry persisted in the view that Bomber Command should have priority over Fighter Command. Prime Minister Baldwin, persuaded by Air Marshals who had fought in the First World War, told the House of Commons in 1932:

I think it is well also for the man in the street to realise that there is no power on earth that can protect him from being bombed. Whatever people may tell him, the bomber will always get through.

In the teeth of all this opposition, Camm presented his mock-up to Air Ministry visitors on 10 January 1935, and on 21 February he sent provisional performance figures to the RAF. The Air Marshals were surprised. The specification called for 275 mph at 15,000 feet. Camm promised 330 mph. When the aircraft returned from its maiden flight and Camm clambered onto the wing, P.W.S. 'George' Bulman, chief test pilot at Hawker Aircraft Limited, said: 'Another winner, I think.' Bulman flew the first prototype, K5083, of what was still known as the 'Interceptor Monoplane' from Brooklands on 6 November 1935. This was the first flight of the Rolls-Royce Merlin engine. Indeed, this Merlin 'C', with its 1,029 bhp and weight of only 1,180 lb, was essential to achieve such a performance. No two-speed, variable pitch propeller had yet been built for such power, so a conventional Watts-designed, two-blade wooden propeller was fitted.

In February 1936, the prototype was delivered for initial service evaluation to the Aircraft and Armament Experimental Establishment at Martlesham Heath, where it was given high marks for reliability. On 3 June, a contract for the production of 600 was received from the Air Ministry. (The company directors had already approved tooling for 1,000.) On 27 June, the aircraft received a new official name, the Hurricane.

As production proceeded apace and the Hurricane proved much more amenable to volume production than the Spitfire, improvements were made constantly as the aircraft were flown and tested. One of the most significant developments was the replacement of the old fixed pitch, two-bladed wooden propeller, which had a tendency to fly into pieces under stress, by a metal, three-bladed, two pitch propeller made by de Havilland. This enabled the pilot to alter the pitch (or angle) of the blades so that he could use fine (low) pitch for take-off and coarse (high) pitch for greater speeds. This brought greater fuel economy and a better rate of climb.

Meanwhile, Rolls-Royce were experiencing the inevitable difficulties in building up production of a consistently reliable Merlin, as is made clear by Harald Penrose in his book *British Aviation – The Ominous Skies 1935–39*:

Martlesham reported on the remarkable ease of handling and good control at all speeds down to stall. A top speed of 315 mph at 16,000 feet was established, thus handsomely beating the Air Staff's requirement of 275 mph. 'The only thing which marred the otherwise very satisfactory trials was continued unreliability of the engine,' said Lucas [the test pilot]. 'There were at least three engine changes during the first two weeks due to a variety of defects, the most serious being internal glycol leaks causing rapid loss of coolant, coupled with distortion and ultimate cracking of cylinder heads because of much higher operating temperatures possible with this type of coolant. Soon it was apparent that the engine required a great deal more development before it became sufficiently reliable for Service operation. All this delayed Martlesham tests and the machine's return to Brooklands for development flying and perform- ance measurements. Meanwhile Rolls-Royce decided that the troubles could only be overcome by intensive flight development with re-designed cylinder heads. We learned that Merlin I engines would not be available for production Hurricanes and that the modified Merlin II would not be ready until autumn of 1937, some three months after the first production Hurricane was due off the line. Worse still, we were told that only a bare minimum of engines would be available to keep the prototype flying.'

Major Bulman at the Air Ministry was all too aware of the teething problems in the production of the Merlin.

Initial Merlin production started well after several type tests were run, but after about 100 engines had been made an epidemic of cracks in the walls of the aluminium combined crankcase and cylinder blocks developed. Hives and ourselves had a desperate investigation into the casting procedure but after an agony of indecision for a few days we decided literally to cut the Gordian knot by splitting the one piece casting into three – crankcase and two cylinder blocks! Frantic tests of the new construction were hurried through, and the trouble disappeared. Production with the drastically modified construction restarted, and thanks to the inevitable setbacks in the output of the first Battles, Hurricanes and Spitfires, Rolls were able to regain their substantial lead in Merlin deliveries to meet the aircraft output. But it was a harassing few months, peace mercifully still prevailing!

As with all military aircraft on both sides, the practicalities of how they performed in combat led to constant changes and improvements. On the Hurricane, increased armour to guard the pilot, additional protection for the engine and linatex covers to make the fuel tanks self-sealing were all welcome, but the real drive was to extract greater performance from the engine and greater power for the guns. Although the Hurricane, with its steel tubular structure and fabric covering, was a more traditional aircraft than the Spitfire, it proved more resistant to exploding cannon shells than its more glamorous fellow fighter.

The Hawker engine design staff considered alternatives to the Merlin engine, but soon realised that a more powerful version of the Merlin itself would be the ideal solution, since it would mean the least modification to the airframe. It was also the most reliable of the engines on offer, and there was a strong moral obligation for Hawker to use the Merlin, since Rolls-Royce had contributed to the cost of the prototype, K5083. By June 1940, after the retreat from Dunkirk but before the Battle of Britain, Hawker had already produced Hurricanes with Merlin IIs and Merlin IIIs. On 11 June, the famous Hawker test-pilot, Philip Lucas, flew an eight-gun Hurricane 1 fitted with a Merlin XX, the engine developed with Stanley Hooker's supercharger. It gave the Hurricane a top speed of 348 mph. Furthermore, the extra power allowed the aircraft to carry four cannons without significant loss of performance.

Although it was the Spitfire and Hurricane that achieved the greatest success and glory in the Second World War, and for which the Merlin was developed and improved out of all recognition from its earliest configuration, the first production order for 200 Merlins was from the Fairey Company for its bomber, the Fairey Battle. The Merlin I was put into production for this aircraft, a single-engined bomber which would carry 1,000 lb of bombs for 1,000 miles at 200 mph. The engines were rated at 1,020 bhp, an output at the time ahead of any other engine in the world.

CHAPTER TWO

'A CHALLENGE OF IMMENSE PROPORTIONS'

FRUSTRATION WITH THE MINISTRY
HIVES PERSUADES FREEMAN
BEAVERBROOK RAISES THE VOLTAGE

FRUSTRATION WITH THE MINISTRY

The original contract for 310 Spitfires called for delivery to begin on 12 October 1937 and to be completed by March 1939, but by April 1939 only 150 had been delivered. The Air Ministry was outraged, effectively accusing Sir Robert McLean of keeping production within Supermarine and failing to use sub-contractors early enough.

The problems of finding sufficiently skilled labour and efficient sub-contractors were not confined to Supermarine. Rolls-Royce were suffering similar difficulties, as is clear from a report by Hives written in October 1937:

People doing sub-contract work have such a choice of work that they will only take on profitable and easy jobs. When they are months behind-hand for the delivery, if we attempt to take any strong measures we are told to take the work away ... The condition of labour is very difficult and we are losing skilled machinists continuously and we are not able to replace them ... There is no skilled labour unemployed.

At the same time, Hives was commercially minded, and he kept a close eye on how Spitfire production was progressing so that Rolls-Royce did not produce engines that would sit around waiting to be purchased. As he reported to his directors:

We think we should be given a lot of credit for the 'timing' of the Merlin production. Although we were bullied and threatened for deliveries 18 months ago, we kept an intelligent eye on the Aircraft Production and timed the Merlin Production so that there would not be a stack of engines piled up in some stores which could have been better and more up to date engines if more time was spent on them.

The Aircraft Constructor cannot deceive us with any optimistic promises. We can make a very accurate estimate of when engines are required, and the fact that we have never kept a machine waiting proves this.

And Hives found, as so many other industrialists have found before and since, that Government departments are notorious for both vacillating over decisions and changing their minds. In his report of 5 December 1938, he said:

Records will prove that Rolls-Royce Limited have always kept their promises to the Air Ministry on deliveries of engines to programme. These records date back to 1915.

The original engine programme for 1938 was for 1,375 Merlin engines plus spares and repairs. At the end of May the programme was reviewed and the output was increased to 1,575 Merlins. At the present time we are approximately 100 engines ahead of programme, and we anticipate that the output of Merlin engines for this year will be approximately 1,700.

Providing a reasonable time is given from the instructions to proceed to the delivery dates, we have no anxiety whatever in producing more and more engines. We feel, however, that our job would be easier if the Air Ministry took us into their confidence and told us of their projected programmes.

Foreign Office Intelligence had changed its mind about Germany's preparedness for war. Original calculations suggested a date sometime in 1942, but in 1936 fresh information indicated that the Germans might be ready as early as January 1939. This was one of the reasons for the rapid signing of contracts for Hurricanes and Spitfires before either had been fully tested. The anger of the Air Ministry might well have been better directed at those who had allowed Britain's aircraft manufacturers to be starved of Government contracts through the 1920s and early 1930s.

Planning for a war while everyone is uncertain as to whether it will break out, and when, indeed, the Government's whole policy is designed to prevent it breaking out, is not easy. However, by early 1939, most intelligent and thoughtful people realised war would be the only way to stop Hitler spreading his pernicious Nazi regime across the whole of Europe and perhaps beyond.

The Air Council had expected war to break out in October 1939 and had estimated that aircraft production would attain the figure of 2,000 per month within eighteen months. Preparations to achieve this began in March 1939 for components and materials, but for airframes and engines existing capacity, enlarged by sub-contracting, was considered to be adequate. The Cabinet held the view that the war would last three years and the Secretary of State for Air, Sir Kingsley Wood, suggested that plans should be made to achieve an output of 3,000 aircraft per month. After the supply of labour had been reviewed this figure was reduced to 2,550 (including a small number from the Dominions). The senior Air Ministry official responsible for aero engine production, Air Chief Marshal Sir Wilfrid Freeman, thought that this target would be reached in June 1942, and that output might ultimately be stepped up to 3,000 by the end of June 1943. At this stage of the war manpower was considered to be the limiting factor. The target for home production was ultimately fixed at 2,425 by July 1942, and became known as the Harrogate programme. But in the early stages of the war this programme had little or no effect on Rolls-Royce. Orders were based on confirmed 'Instructions to Proceed' (ITPs) and the total of engines for which ITPs had been received was well below the total required by the various programmes now being issued with ever-increasing frequency.

In September 1939 there were four main aero engine firms – Rolls-Royce, Armstrong Siddeley, Bristols and Napier – and six shadow factories, excluding Crewe, which came under the direct administration of the parent company, and Glasgow, which started the production of parts in the middle of 1940 and produced its first complete engine in November. All pre-war estimates of the capacity of these factories were based on the assumption of single-shift working. The main combat aircraft of the Royal Air Force were largely powered by Bristol and Rolls-Royce engines, and the training and auxiliary aircraft by Armstrong Siddeley and de Havilland engines. Napiers had produced no engines of any great importance after their 'Lion', though the 'Sabre' was beginning to attract considerable attention at the Air Ministry in 1939.

Between January and the end of August 1939 Derby had produced 1,357 engines, the great majority of which were Merlins. A radial air-cooled engine designed primarily for the new Fairey Fleet Air Arm aircraft and known as the Boreas or Exe was under development but not in production. The Peregrine (a supercharged Kestrel), the Vulture (a 24-cylinder X) and the Griffon (a Merlin scaled up to the same dimensions as the original 'R') were under development at Derby and work was in progress on a two-stroke engine and on compression ignition. Orders for these engines during 1939 had been based, albeit rather vaguely, on the 'L' scheme, and in February Hives (General Manager and effectively the chief executive in charge of aero engine production) informed Sir Wilfrid Freeman that the firm was 'planning to produce the equivalent of 600 Merlins per month in 12 months' time'. This estimate did not include the Glasgow factory, which was not scheduled to come into production until late 1940, a timetable which proved optimistic by two months. In the event there was no sudden rise in output towards the latter part of

1939 or early in 1940 and though there were many reasons for this, which are discussed below, the fact is that the absorption of engines into aircraft was substantially lower than the Air Ministry's demands that output should be further increased and capacity further expanded.

At the beginning of 1939 the confirmed orders for Derby were expected to produce an output of 3,200 engines (almost entirely Merlins) by March 1940. Follow-on orders left a total of 4,900 engines (400 of which were Vultures) to be completed after this, and the company was warned that it might also be asked to produce no less than 1,600 Peregrines for the Whirlwind. The Air Ministry was unable to give a clear indication of its future requirements until after the outbreak of war and all attempts during the early part of the year to obtain a delivery programme extending beyond March 1940 failed to produce any results.

During June and July 1939, however, the view that aircraft output would ultimately be limited by engine output began to crystallise at the Air Ministry. Despite the rapidly increasing gap between output and absorption in airframes, Air Marshal Tedder, as he was then, told W. Lappin, the firm's special representative at the Ministry, that he estimated there would be a shortage of 1,000 Merlins by June 1940. The position was confusing to management since the requirements of the various programmes (of which no less than six were received in 1939 alone) varied greatly and were often apparently unrelated to the plans of the aircraft manufacturers, most of whom kept in direct touch with Derby.

As war became imminent, the question of contract cover ceased to be of much significance since it became quite reasonable to assume that this had become a mere formality. In August the 'all-out' instructions began to come in from the Air Ministry. On the 26th Sir Henry Self informed the Managing Director, Sir Arthur Sidgreaves, that it was 'of vital importance in the national interest that every practicable step be taken immediately to intensify production of aircraft and aeronautical material of all kinds required for the R.A.F'.

HIVES PERSUADES FREEMAN

On 28 August Sir Wilfrid Freeman wrote to Hives stressing the view that engines would be the main factor limiting the supply of aircraft to the RAF. 'I realise', he said, 'that you have done a great deal towards improving the position but if there are any further steps you can take to improve output, and if there is any way in which I can help, or if you have any suggestions to make towards a solution of the problems which are outside your control, I hope you will not hesitate to inform me.'

This prompted an immediate reply in which Hives discussed the various ways in which output from the Rolls-Royce group might be increased. The very high Air Ministry (AID) inspection standards resulted in a lot of scrapped materials which he thought could be turned into perfectly satisfactory and reliable engines. Lead-bronze bearings, for example, were scrapped if they were found to have blow-holes, and these made no difference to their performance or reliability. 'For years', he said, 'we have made a practice of running engines built up with parts which have been scrapped by the A.I.D., and therefore we have that experience to draw upon.' The high quality of screw-threads demanded on certain parts where it was not really necessary restricted the output of sub-contractors who were not used to high-precision work. External finish was costly and time-consuming and did not affect the life or performance of the engine in the least. The Royal Air Force would gain, he suggested, by relying much more fully on Rolls-Royce engineers: 'The main point we wish to stress is that we have the knowledge and experience and should be given the power to say which parts should be used.'

In the same memorandum Hives made several further recommendations of great practical importance. He asked that Rolls-Royce should be given the power to requisition all sub-contractors' plant and to transfer this plant from one factory to another if this was considered to be necessary in the interests of maximum production. The next recommendation (which was immediately adopted and proved an outstanding success) was that a Rolls-Royce service engineer, who would report back directly to Derby, should be attached to every squadron flying aircraft fitted with Rolls-Royce engines. Even before official approval for this had been given, a group of service engineers had left for France. The remaining recommendations concerned engines under development. Though Hives thought that the development of the Vulture, Boreas and Peregrine should be suspended, he was strongly in favour of continuing work on the Griffon, an engine whose overall dimensions and design were similar to the Merlin, which it could replace in several types of aircraft without serious modification to the airframe.

Sir Wilfrid Freeman agreed immediately to most of these suggestions. He was not altogether happy about suspending work on the Boreas, which was urgently required for Fairey naval aircraft, but Hives pointed out that the effort required to produce 275 Boreas engines was equivalent to 1,200 Merlins and outlined a somewhat novel form of the conflict between firm and state.

If we take the Rolls-Royce point of view it would be in our interests to proceed with the production of that engine. We have done three or four years' work on it: – we are satisfied that as a type it has considerable merit over the radial sleeve-valve engine and we are definitely going to be the losers if the production of this engine is held up. From a national point of view, however, we think it would be wrong to proceed with this engine.

Freeman was persuaded and agreed to suspend work on the Boreas. Work on the Vulture had to continue, since it was assumed that the Manchester bomber and the Tornado fighter would use this engine. During the first few weeks of the war there was considerable uncertainty over the Peregrine. The order was first reduced, then increased, and finally cancelled. The Air Ministry was also unable to reach a clear decision about the Merlin-engined Wellington bomber. The Alvis Company had already started a powerplant production line to adapt Merlins to this aircraft, and after considerable discussion it was decided that the work should proceed. The Air Ministry wished to suspend the Merlin Wellington on the grounds that there would be a very great expansion of the output of other types of aircraft for which no alternative engine existed; but Rolls-Royce was under no illusions, and it was realised that it would be a complete waste of resources if these engines were not used.

In the first week of September the whole organisation at Derby and Crewe was keyed up for the onslaught. It was naturally expected that aero engine firms would be one of the highest-priority targets of the Luftwaffe and despite the dislocation involved in the transfer of staff there was a record output of 74 Merlins (of which nine were produced at Crewe). But the onslaught did not materialise and the people of Britain realised that the German armed forces were to be otherwise occupied for some time. For most people there was a sensation of 'back to normal'. The war did not greatly upset the customary routines of existence and this attitude reduced the sense of urgency and the flexibility which this induces, until the full weight of the Reichswehr was thrown into the attack on France. Only then was it realised that half-measures and total war were incompatible.

Though the psychological conditions of the 'Phoney War' inhibited an immediate nation-wide response, there were, fortunately, a good many responsible people in the Ministries and at Rolls-Royce who were not deceived by the slow tempo of the first few months. They realised that in due course the demands which the industry would be called upon to meet would tax its capacity to the utmost. The existing capacity, though quite capable of fulfilling current orders, was unlikely to be able to meet the demands of the global air war which the realists foresaw to be inevitable as soon as Hitler had conquered Europe. Though Hives was in full agreement with the Ministry's view that capacity would have to be increased he did not consider that equipping completely new factories was the best way to do it.

At least both the aircraft and the aero engine manufacturers now had a few months to build up production before the

1. Hives as a boy with his family in the late 1890s.
STANDING LEFT TO RIGHT: Henry, Ethel, John (Jack),
Frederick (Fred), Elizabeth (Lizzie), William (Will).
SITTING LEFT TO RIGHT: Matthew (Matt), Mary Jane (Janie),
John, Mary (née Washbourn), Margaret (Maggie), Mabel.
ON THE GROUND: Ernest (Ern) and Beatrice (Beattie).

2. A Rolls-Royce Kestrel engine, critical in re-establishing Rolls-Royce's position as the premier supplier of aero engines to the RAF at the end of the 1920s.

3. Merlin supercharger drive wheelcases being assembled in the late 1930s.

4. A Merlin engine being built shortly before war
broke out in September 1939.

5. Spitfires from 65 Squadron, Hornchurch, during
the Battle of Britain in the summer of 1940, all powered
by Merlin engines.

POST OFFICE
TELEGRAM

Charges to pay
s. d.
RECEIVED

No.
OFFICE STAMP

DERBY

Prefix. Time handed in. Office of Origin and Service Instructions. Words. 4 JUL 40

From _____ 94   394   F.O LONDON TELEX 102   To _____

THE MANAGER ROYCAR DERBY

WILL YOU PLEASE TELL YOUR STAFF THAT I WILL WELCOME AND
REJOICE IN A DECISION BY THEM TO STAY AT THEIR POST AFTER THE
SIRENS SOUND AND UNTIL THE DANGER OF BOMB ATTACK IS IMMINENT
STOP SUCH A DEMONSTRATION OF COURAGE AND DEVOTION WOULD IN A
LARGE MEASURE DEFEAT THE ENEMYS PURPOSE OF DAMAGING OUR
PRODUCTION FOR DEFENCE STOP IF EVERY FACTORY IS A CITADEL OF
RESOLUTION MEN, SUSTAINING BY THEIR LABOURS THE PILOTS AND
CREWS WHO BATTLE FOR US IN THE SKIES, BRITAIN WILL HURL BACK

POST OFFICE
TELEGRAM

Charges to pay
s. d.
RECEIVED

No.
OFFICE STAMP

Prefix. Time handed in. Office of Origin and Service Instructions. Words.

From _____   To _____

THE ONSLAUGHT OF OUR ENEMIES AND SAVE THE WORLD
FOR FREEDOM = BEAVERBROOK +

For free repetition of doubtful words telephone " TELEGRAMS ENQUIRY " or call, with this form
at office of delivery. Other enquiries should be accompanied by this form and, if possible, the envelope.

6. A telegram from the Minister, Lord Beaverbrook.

7. A Merlin prototype being assembled in the Experimental
Department in Derby in 1943.

8. An Armstrong Whitworth Whitley bomber
powered by Merlin Xs, the first Merlin with the two-speed
supercharger drive.

Phoney War became real war with Hitler's invasion of Denmark and Norway in early April 1940. The British troops in Norway (originally on their way to Finland to help the Finns against the Russians) were forced to evacuate. As Peter Hennessy wrote in his book *Never Again: Britain 1945–51*, 'The development of British forces in Norway ... was chaotic in conception, confused in execution and humiliating in its outcome.'

The Prime Minister, Neville Chamberlain, lost the confidence of his party and was replaced by Winston Churchill, who had long predicted the war and who had been urging re-armament for nearly ten years.

In the House of Commons on 13 May 1940, in perhaps his most quoted and memorable speech, he said:

I would say to the House, as I said to those who have joined this government: I have nothing to offer but blood, toil, tears and sweat.

We have before us an ordeal of the most grievous kind. We have before us many, many long months of struggle and of suffering. You ask what is our policy? I will say: it is to wage war against a monstrous tyranny, never surpassed in the dark, lamentable catalogue of human crime. That is our policy.

You ask, what is our aim? I can answer in one word: it is victory, victory at all costs, victory in spite of all terror, victory, however long and hard the road may be; for without victory there is no survival.

Victory was not going to be easy, as soon became apparent when the German forces swept with ease through Holland and Belgium and into France. The Dutch and Belgian air forces were virtually destroyed within hours and many of the 275 day fighters and 70 bombers available to the French Air Force were destroyed on the ground. In spite of being a leader in the early days of the aircraft industry, France had fallen woefully behind in the 1920s and 1930s so that by 1940 its 600 fighters were outclassed by the Messerschmitt Bf 109. Nor were many of the British aircraft in France, such as the Fairey Battle, a match for it.

There were six squadrons comprising 96 Hurricanes, which

were a match for the Luftwaffe, but more were needed. Dowding, charged with the defence of Britain, resisted the appeals to send more, knowing that he would need every aircraft for that defence if the battle for France was lost.

That battle was indeed lost and on 22 June the French signed an armistice at Compiègne in the same railway wagon in which the German generals had accepted defeat in 1918. As Churchill said: 'The Battle for France is over, the Battle of Britain is about to begin.'

There were no more than 331 Hurricanes and Spitfires available, supported by 150 outdated other fighters – Blenheims, Defiants and Gladiators. Fortunately, the Germans also needed some time to re-group and a six-week pause ensued before the onslaught on Britain began.

This was a vital respite which allowed the RAF to build up its fighter force to 60 squadrons of 654 aircraft, 49 of the squadrons (565 aircraft) consisting of Hurricanes and Spitfires.

BEAVERBROOK RAISES THE VOLTAGE

In February 1940, as a result of a careful reassessment of German aircraft production made for the Chief of Air Staff, the Secretary of State for Air, Sir Samuel Hoare, had decided that the British target of 2,550 aircraft per month would have to be reviewed. There seemed little hope of obtaining the desired increase without a sacrifice of some of the newer machines which were scheduled to come forward in 1941. While the reformulation of this target was under discussion the attack on France began and it was soon realised that the demands which the Air Ministry had originally expected to be made on the Air Force in September 1939 would now have to be met in full. The intensity of the crisis mounted with great rapidity and within a few weeks all production had to be drastically reoriented towards supplying the insatiable needs of the RAF. Fighter Command had no choice but to commit the whole of its front-line strength to the defence of the corridor from Dunkirk, and, very shortly thereafter, to containing the onslaught of the Luftwaffe in the Battle of Britain.

On 10 May, when Chamberlain was succeeded by Churchill, Lord Beaverbrook became Minister of Aircraft Production. Beaverbrook has been well described by Commander Stephen King-Hall as the man whose personality raised the voltage at the Ministry of Aircraft Production, and throughout the entire aircraft industry, to a potential far higher than it had ever carried before. Though this voltage – which no civil service system of organisation and administration had ever been designed to carry – may have blown a large number of fuses in important parts of the structure, it nevertheless ensured that for several crucial months the RAF was able to tap the industrial resources of the country to a degree which would certainly not otherwise have been possible. It was also important that the industry should have a sense of participation in the conflict.

Rolls-Royce soon felt the impact of the new Minister. His aggressive realism was very much in sympathy with the outlook at Derby. There may have been considerable disagreement over details and methods but there was no real disharmony between Lord Beaverbrook and the management. Both disliked the mistrusted civil service routines and programmes, and the ideal of careful calculation which, however admirable from the point of view of Government, ignored the all-important problem of time. In April, the month before Lord Beaverbrook took office, Derby produced 204 Merlins, Crewe 185. The output of repaired engines was 130. By the end of June the Derby output had increased to 494, that of Crewe to 345, and that of repaired engines to 292. The total output of both factories fell slightly in July and again in August, but the output of repaired engines was increased to 327. The fighter squadrons which fought over Dunkirk and later in the Battle of Britain were entirely engined by the Merlin. The Hurricane predominated, followed by the Spitfire and the Defiant. The main mark of Merlin in production at this time was the Mk.X although production of the Mk.XX was just starting at Derby. The new engines produced during the period June–October were not the engines which fought the great air battles of these months, but damaged engines had to be repaired and replaced, and, where possible, the opportunity was taken during repair to introduce the latest modifications based on the experience which was being gained from intensive operation. In the rectification of faults which came to light only under service conditions the immediate liaison of the Rolls-Royce engineers at squadrons with the technical staff at Derby proved invaluable. The big output of repaired engines at this time was largely due to the efforts of R.N. Dorey, the senior engineer at Hucknall, who within a few weeks developed, on his own initiative, extensive repair and modification facilities. The whole organisation was a miracle of improvisation devoted to the single objective of getting the maximum number of aircraft back into the air in fighting trim.

There was a substantial repair organisation in place by June 1940. Merlins were being repaired and, in some cases, part manufactured at the factories of the de Havilland, Alvis, Talbot and Napier companies, as well as at Derby, Belper, Glasgow and the Manchester Ford Works. Hucknall's main function was to provide facilities for handling the great increase in repair work which suddenly took place during the crisis months of 1940.

Three problems confronted Lord Beaverbrook. The first was to keep the front-line squadrons up to strength and, if possible, to increase their number. The second was to keep the performance of these aircraft ahead of that of the enemy. This was as much an administrative as a technical problem since the higher performance always existed on the drawing-board, on the test-bench or in the prototype. It sometimes existed in the production line. But there was a limit to the speed at which any one stage could be pushed on to the next. The greater the speed, the greater the dislocation of current production and, to some extent, future output. Each stage between the drawing-board and the production line could be missed out but there was no means of calculating the risk involved in missing out one or several stages. The risk was always considerable but from time to time it had to be taken. The third problem was to ensure that present performance and present production were not gained at the expense of future performance and future production.

The first problem was purely internal in character – a question of creating the conditions under which the existing system could achieve the maximum output. This was done by imposing some restrictions and lifting others. The second problem was related to the performance of enemy aircraft and the tactical purposes for which these were being employed. Speed, altitude, endurance and firepower determined the nature and outcome of the war in the air. The third problem was a question of judging the margin, if any, which the urgency of the present left for consideration of the future.

Lord Beaverbrook's first step was to concentrate production on five types of aircraft – the Wellington, Whitley, Hurricane, Spitfire and Blenheim. A similar rationalisation of engine production was proposed by the Chief Executive at the MAP, Sir Charles Craven, who had been brought in from Vickers. Craven endeavoured to persuade the industry and the Ministries that the number of engines under development and in production should be reduced to three liquid-cooled and three radial. The main liquid-cooled engines under development were the Merlin, the Griffon and the Vulture, produced by Rolls-Royce, and the Sabre, produced by Napiers. The Griffon and Vulture were both candidates for the bowler hat, but Hives would not agree at this stage to their abandonment, although it was not long before he thought it advisable to allow the Vulture to drop out.

At a meeting on 22 June, attended by all the important firms in the industry, Sir Charles Craven pointed out that this was a long-term project which had on no account to interfere with current production. Hives objected to the whole proposal on the grounds that there was no point in trying to rationalise the engine programme until a 'clear-cut and stable' aircraft programme had been decided upon. But there was no possibility of this happening under Lord Beaverbrook, who was of the firm opinion that the waste which was bound to be incurred in the endeavour of each firm to produce an 'unco-ordinated' maximum output was preferable to the lower overall volume of production which a carefully planned and controlled programme might have achieved without waste. In view of the serious inadequacy of the whole apparatus of centralised control at this stage of the war this was undoubtedly the correct policy. An industrial system which is producing at full blast, even if parts of it are producing in different directions, at least affords firms an opportunity to develop their maximum individual output, and it is always easier to cut down production in some sectors than to build it up in others. Beaverbrook's policy naturally implied the conclusion that the overall planning mechanism was deficient, mainly because the almost infinite complexities of the apparatus had not been appreciated. But Beaverbrook realised that the margin was so narrow that in the interests of immediate production even the relatively minor drags – physical and psychological – which the contemporary efforts to develop an apparatus of co-ordination and control had imposed on the system should be abandoned. He gave instructions that all development work was to cease (an instruction which was fortunately not obeyed indiscriminately). These instructions were all somewhat exaggerated, but their tenor was much more than their content. Ill-judged but vigorous instructions, provided they are sufficiently specific and drastic, will often convey the necessary impression to those who have the expert knowledge to transform them into effective action.

To encourage production several restrictions were raised. On 24 May the Air Ministry asked for a works committee consisting of the Air Ministry overseer, a production officer, the firm's chief inspector and a representative of the works management to be set up with full executive powers to alter inspection procedure in the interests of maximum production. The Merlin III was given top priority at Derby. A double-shift seven-day week was introduced and except for two half-hour breaks at the change of shifts the factories were in continuous operation. The day shift was from 8 a.m. to 8 p.m. and the night shift from 8.30 p.m. to 7.30 a.m. Thus in a working week of 161 hours, 69 hours of overtime were worked. For certain classes of labour, the hours worked exceeded the statutory maximum, but despite protests from Ministry of Labour officials, the management decided that, provided the employees agreed to do so, the effort should be made. There was no dissent. Lord Beaverbrook was informed of this decision and supported it. This pace was kept up until late in 1941 when it was decided that the effort was proving too costly in terms of sickness and absenteeism.

On 28 May the Minister telegraphed that he had issued instructions 'to postpone all unnecessary returns forthwith'. Only output returns were to be made to the Ministry. On the following day he telegraphed that 'instructions will shortly be issued which will facilitate the financial situation for contractors and sub-contractors'. On 22 June, just after Dunkirk, when the invasion threat began to loom ahead, he wrote a characteristically melodramatic letter to Hives giving him virtually dictatorial powers in the event of a direct enemy attack:

I appoint you Chairman of a Committee of One required to deal with Rolls-Royce properties in the case of enemy attack. You have complete authority and discretion in the organisation of R.R. output on such terms and conditions as you desire. Your authority will also extend to all sub-contractors of Rolls-Royce whose works may be subjected to enemy attack.

Lord Beaverbrook was receptive to constructive suggestion and not in the least afraid, simply because they had come from the industry itself, of adopting suggestions which appeared reasonable. Before the Blitz struck, Hives had written to Air Commodore H. Peake, a newly elected director of the firm, who had just been appointed Director of Public Relations at the Air Ministry, commenting on the poor publicity which the services, and indirectly the products of industry, were receiving. This was having a bad effect on industrial morale. 'The men are getting bored with this war', he said; 'we have never had a single bit of information from the Air Ministry which would interest our workers.' In consequence Rolls-Royce made arrangements for the firm's own employees who

51

had been in France to broadcast over the factory loudspeaker system and Sidgreaves suggested to the Minister that RAF pilots should be brought to the factories to recount their experiences. Beaverbrook replied that he had taken note of all these suggestions and that he had appointed Beverly Baxter, MP, in charge of publicity and propaganda.

There has been disagreement over whether Beaverbrook should take *all* the credit for the rapid expansion of aircraft and engine production. Alex Henshaw (still thriving in Newmarket near Cambridge in his 90s), the test pilot on the spot at the Spitfire factory at Castle Bromwich, was obviously close to events on the ground but could not have been privy to the councils of war in Whitehall and Downing Street. He wrote in his book *Sigh for a Merlin*:

Strange as it may seem today, the Spitfire was not accepted with alacrity. No one would doubt its speed and handling qualities but many doubted its armament potentiality and harboured grave doubts about the feasibility of mass producing such an advanced aircraft. This ominous doubt was reinforced to some extent by the huge Nuffield factory at Castle Bromwich, specifically built to turn out fighters and bombers on a prodigious scale [William Morris, created Baron Nuffield in 1938, had built up his very successful Morris Motors Ltd. between the wars, and had been an obvious candidate to operate a shadow factory]. The frustrating problems and difficulties encountered at this factory, in spite of modern equipment and a vast workforce, seemed insuperable. It all came to a crisis point when France collapsed and the mighty German blitz swept us to the Channel ports.

Our backs were now to the wall – we needed weapons of every description but most of all we needed fighter aircraft.

One can only speculate upon what might have happened had Nuffield remained in charge of this vital source of supply. It was fortuitous that the dynamic, ruthless and astute Lord Beaverbrook came into power at this time as Minister of Aircraft Production. Ruthless he may have been, but it is very doubtful whether anyone else was really alive to the situation that faced us or had the ability and guts to handle an industry under such conditions.

Aware that the very survival of the Free World could depend only upon our own efforts and with the War daily taking a more depressing and ominous turn, heads had to roll and Beaverbrook was certainly the man to chop them off.

He trapped Nuffield into a situation where his resignation was irrevocable. He then called in Supermarine, the only aircraft company which could possibly alleviate what was rapidly becoming a national scandal.

From the time I had arrived in Southampton in November 1939 until May the following year, the Nuffield progress with the Spitfire Mk II was pitiful. Therefore, when Supermarine were handed this headless giant on a plate, it represented a somewhat frightening challenge of immense proportions. It did not help matters when feelings between the two organisations became strained and not exactly harmonious.

There is no doubt in my mind that but for the intervention of Lord Beaverbrook and the handing over of the Nuffield factory administration to Vickers-Armstrongs and the Supermarine organisation, many of whom were sent up to Castle Bromwich, we might well have been invaded before a single aircraft had flown from the factory.

On the other hand, Sholto Douglas, about to take over from Dowding as Commander in Chief, Fighter Command, disagreed strongly when Prime Minister Churchill recorded in a minute to the Secretary of State for Air on 3 June 1940: 'Lord Beaverbrook has made a surprising improvement in the supply of aeroplanes, and in clearing up the muddle and scandal of the Aircraft Production branch.' Douglas thought it another example of Churchill's 'genius for self-deception' and grossly unfair to Wilfrid Freeman, who had taken over from Dowding as Air Member for Research and Development at the Air Ministry on 1 April 1936. In Douglas's view, Freeman had achieved miracles in these four years, bringing the Spitfire and Hurricane to the point of readiness for battle, setting up the radar network which was to prove so vital to Britain's survival, and laying down the plans for the four-engined bombers.

Freeman himself, as Anthony Furse made clear in his

Wilfrid Freeman, The Genius behind Allied Survival and Air Supremacy 1939 to 1945, was:

Frustrated by months of inaction from Nuffield, Welsh and Courtney (Air Marshals on the Air Council Supply Committee), Freeman admired the ruthless way Beaverbrook forced through the administrative changes which transferred the entire salvage and repair organisation to the MAP.

Freeman said of Beaverbrook:

I wouldn't have believed it was possible for anyone to go on as [Beaverbrook] does, day after day, with only six hours off. His house is always packed, mostly with politicians, [but with] a sprinkling of industrialists. The odds against us at times seem overwhelming; that's one advantage in the Beaver, he does lessen the odds and over-ride difficulties as no other politician would do, or even dare to attempt.

John (later Air Chief Marshal Sir John) Slessor agreed with Douglas. In his capacity as Director of Plans, Air Ministry from 1937 until 1941, he was in a position to observe Freeman's contribution closely. He said later:

The original responsibility for the Battle of Britain Fighters was not Freeman's – they were already decided on before he came into the Air Ministry. The original Shadow factory scheme – based on the motor-car industry – was also initiated before his time. But the development and production of the HURRICANE and SPITFIRE were his responsibility. He presided over the whole tremendous expansion of orders for all types from 1936 to the middle of 1940. He sponsored the great extensions of the 'Shadow' factories, and the creation of a vast reserve of manufacturing capacity. And he developed to the utmost the design resources of what were known as the 'family' firms.

But there were many developments of vital importance during the years of 1936 to 1939 for which the responsibility and the credit lay with Freeman. Hundred octane fuel – the Variable Pitch propellor [*sic*] – the air rocket, for instance. And, above all, the initiation of the four-engined bomber policy. I well remember, as Director of Plans, the excitement and interest of discussing with him, his proposals for the first production orders of those aircraft, which were destined to have such a tremendous influence on the outcome of the war.

And Slessor added:

A man who was in a better position than most people to know – Lord Hives of Rolls-Royce – has written to me – 'it was the expansion which was carried out under Wilfrid's direction in 1937/39 which enabled the Battle of Britain to be won. Without that foresight and imagination, no efforts in 1940 would have yielded any results.'

Furthermore, asked Douglas, how could Beaverbrook make such a dramatic improvement when he had only been appointed three weeks earlier? Major Bulman, promoted by Freeman in October 1938 to oversee all engine and propeller production for the Air Ministry, wrote of Beaverbrook's contribution:

Lord Beaverbrook's name will always be associated with the tremendous explosion in aeronautical production which followed his appointment as the M.A.P. Much indeed was owed to his dynamism and readiness at any time to tear up any previous agreement or understanding which seemed to him to get in his way in grabbing every priority or potential source of material like an impish pirate with complete disregard for any resultant side effects. Some credit may also be accorded to the Air Ministry team he had inherited (and hadn't already figuratively executed!) who by a super effort sweated to maintain the fundamental machinery of production they had built up during the preceding years, often concealing from their Master some aspects of it, lest he trampled on them.

In calm retrospect one can only conjecture how much the build-up of output following Dunkirk would have occurred without his unique personality. How much was due to the summation of effort by every man and woman in the Industry in the face of the menace of Hitler, working often till they dropped from sheer exhaustion, achieving unknowingly their Finest Hour, with that unity of purpose and self sacrifice which only War can inspire in the Nation? All the tools had been laid down in the years before, producing a rapidly accelerating output, further escalated by the hearts of ordinary men and women inspired by Winston Churchill's magical broadcasts and the direness of the cataclysm erupting during 1940. Rome was not built in a day; or by the genius of one man.

The answer probably lies somewhere in between these opposing views of Beaverbrook's contribution. He undoubtedly did step up aircraft production, but not by 3 June 1940.

Whatever other people's view of Beaverbrook, Rolls-Royce, and especially Hives, responded well to a man who, in modern parlance, 'cut out the crap'; or, as Commander Stephen King-Hall (who had done so much to alert everyone to the Nazi threat during the 1930s) put it more delicately, 'raised the voltage at the Ministry of Aircraft Production'.

George Bulman, who was Head of Engine Development at the Air Ministry in the 1930s, had certainly worked closely with all the aero engine manufacturers in the 1930s long before Beaverbrook was involved. In his memoirs, published by the Rolls-Royce Heritage Trust, he wrote:

Monthly meetings at Bristol involved an underlying tension of personalities and clashes between Fedden and his staff. If – as was not infrequent – I, representing the Service and the Air Ministry, did not agree with a proposal submitted, there resulted often long and quite futile argument or at least a period of barely concealed annoyance. One emerged ... from hours of psychological warfare, utterly spent.

At Derby we used to argue no less and beat out decisions purely on their technical merits, but the atmosphere was quite different. There were joyous scraps, like amateur boxing contests, hard knocks given and received with a mutual grin, from which at the end of a long day one went home physically and mentally stimulated.

Meetings at Derby were generally preceded by travelling up the previous evening, usually with Bill Lappin in a Rolls or Bentley (which he would let me drive). Lappin was virtually a private agent to Hives. He was always in constant touch with squadrons equipped with Rolls engines, anticipating their worries and mingling, light-heartedly but always effectively, with all who were, or might be, concerned with new projects in which his firm might perhaps play a part or give help. He would talk with Air Marshals and with AC2s in a squadron workshop with equal respect and goodwill. He was a veritable encyclopaedia of current and often future Service affairs, and ubiquitous in seeking his information.

Rolls had a delightful guesthouse at Duffield Bank, a few miles north, overlooking the Derwent River, at which I usually stayed the night in great comfort and relaxation. An admirable dinner would ensue with Sidgreaves, Hives and about ten of his people; Rowledge and A G Elliott the designer, Stanley Hooker (before he went to Bristol), Swift the production man, Dorey the installation man, whose supreme art lay in his ability to find out weakness in the design materials by flogging an engine on the test bed until something broke. He was a tough but modest character who had come from Siddeleys, a terrific but heartbreaking asset.

Conversation at dinner would be light-hearted, drifting to flying topics only occasionally, followed by hilarious snooker and darts at which Hives was equally a great performer. Yet during these hours of relaxation and complete informality, exchanges of thought leading to mutual understandings were often made, to the ultimate good of the Service, as one imagines often occurs in the field of the highest diplomacy, far from the glare of publicity.

CHAPTER THREE

THE SHADOW FACTORIES

ROLLS-ROYCE AGREE WITH THE SHADOW SCHEME
LONG AND FRUSTRATING DELAYS
'DO NOT REFER ME TO ANOTHER GOVERNMENT DEPARTMENT'
FORD AS WELL

ROLLS-ROYCE AGREE WITH THE SHADOW SCHEME

As the Government gradually realised during the 1930s the necessity for re-armament it also realised the need for new factories dedicated to achieving the required output of aircraft, engines, guns and tanks. The Government turned to the motor car companies because of their experience of mass production but for aero engines Rolls-Royce was an obvious candidate for assistance. Hives was only too keen to co-operate but he had to persuade the Rolls-Royce board, who initially opposed the idea on the grounds that technical information would be disclosed to competitors. When it came to the needs of his country Hives, though a Rolls-Royce man through and through, was not going to let parochial competition prevent companies working together for the greater good. Later, when Sir Stanley Hooker was working on the Merlin supercharger, he allowed Roy Fedden from Bristol to send a team to Derby to learn the secret. Nevertheless, he wanted the Government to realise the scale of the challenge. It was not just a question of replicating their factory in Derby. He wrote:

The Rolls-Royce factory at Derby has been built and developed around the problem of producing high-class engineering in relatively small quantities with the capacity to change or modify the product quickly. In other words, I should describe the Derby factory as a huge development factory rather than a manufacturing plant. The very structure of the organisation necessitates a large proportion of skilled men who fortunately are available.

As a super aircraft engine development factory there is nothing like it in the world, and therefore in planning for the very big production we want to make sure that Derby is used to the very best advantage. In any big scheme we consider that Derby should be expected to carry all the development work; it should also carry the prototype production over the first two or three hundred engines until all the engineering 'bugs' in the new type of engine have been cleared. It would also have to be responsible for all the inevitable jobs which it is impossible to avoid such as odd spares, changeovers and modifications. This class of work can be done at Derby but upsets the whole scheme of things in a true manufacturing plant.

The production at Crewe has been planned on very different lines to Derby. We are making use of very much more unskilled and semi-skilled labour. There is no doubt we could go further, but we do not wish to have any trouble with labour. Crewe cannot absorb modifications and alterations like the Derby plant. It would be very much more expensive in both tools and delays.

There is no mystery or fundamental difficulty in producing Rolls-Royce engines with unskilled labour. It means a longer time in planning the production, more expense on jigs, tools and fixtures, the co-operation of the machine tool makers, freedom from alterations, and a longer time before production can commence. We could never hope to obtain sufficient skilled men at Crewe if we were using the same ratio as we are at Derby.

It must be appreciated that the Crewe factory was planned to make more use of sub-contractors than we do at Derby. For instance, it has no pattern shop or foundry and no drop forge; it does not produce crankshafts, camshafts, cylinder liners, pistons or gears. We were able to sub-contract these parts successfully to look after the first portion of Crewe but now we have started on the second portion we find that we shall have to produce in that unit a number of parts which were not originally planned for because we have failed to get the necessary numbers from sub-contractors.

If it is decided to go ahead with another factory we recommend that it be located in Scotland, preferably near Glasgow. We have had one of our men up there who has located a suitable site ... The chief advantage in going to Glasgow is that labour should be available. It should also be available for whatever size it is decided to make the factory. We have definitely decided against recommending any further extensions at Crewe because there is insufficient labour to draw upon, and, so far, insufficient houses ...

Another advantage of Glasgow is that we are now planning to obtain supplies of steel and forgings from Scottish firms and we feel confident that they will prove satisfactory.

LONG AND FRUSTRATING DELAYS

Nevertheless, Hives, convinced like Churchill since the early 1930s that war with Germany was inevitable, had been a strong advocate of shadow factories, and had written to Lieutenant-Colonel H.A.P. Disney of the Directorate of Aeronautical Production at the Air Ministry on 9 October 1937:

I notice that you have already received a note from Sidgreaves saying that Rolls-Royce are in agreement with the Shadow Scheme. Actually I go further, and I am going to pester you until the shadowing of Rolls-Royce engines is an accomplished fact. I want to assure you that whenever the decision is taken I shall make it my personal job to see that you have our 100 per cent co-operation, and that we go out of our way to make it a success.

The company was to experience long and frustrating delays in bringing its Crewe and Glasgow workforces up to the level of skill required. Moving skilled personnel from Derby also proved difficult, not least in the provision of adequate housing.

Nevertheless, operating in the factory at Hillington near Glasgow built and run by the Government, Rolls-Royce benefited from lessons learnt in starting up the factory at Crewe. Construction began in June 1939 and the first building was occupied in October, one month after the outbreak of war. Planned output for Glasgow was greater than that for Crewe, and the factory was specifically designed to ensure a smooth flow of production. Machine tools were arranged and set for single-purpose operations and line production. An important distinction between the two shadow factories was that Glasgow was designed to be almost completely independent of sub-contract activity. This aim was successfully achieved. In 1941 Glasgow machined 98 per cent of its production, compared with 51 per cent at Derby and 57 per cent at Crewe. Glasgow also manufactured its own castings, and was equipped with the most modern light-alloy foundry in the country. By the end of September 1940 the whole factory was occupied. With 16,000 employees, it was one of the largest industrial operations in Scotland.

The Hillington factory was an undertaking of no small magnitude from any point of view. Labour presented one of the most difficult problems and was energetically tackled from the outset. Arrangements were made for the Stow Technical College to train apprentices, a toolroom was established near the site for the training of fitters, and eight standard factory units were rented from the Hillington industrial estate to provide a factory in which machines could be put into operation for both training and production as soon as possible. The foundry presented by far the biggest labour problem. This type of work was completely unknown in Scotland and experienced coremakers and dressers were unobtainable elsewhere in the country. It was therefore decided to make the maximum possible use of specially trained female labour and to minimise the demand for highly skilled labour by employing the most modern mechanised methods of foundry production. Wherever possible all materials were handled mechanically. This in itself necessitated the development of all-metal pattern equipment, which was unknown to the pattern-making industry in Scotland. To make this possible local pattern-makers were sent to acquire the techniques employed at Coventry and specially selected men were given a course of training in foundry work at Derby, where the metallurgical and foundry techniques had been developed to an exceptionally high standard.

In this and many other ways the management implemented its promise to the Air Ministry to place the skill and resources of Rolls-Royce at the disposal of the nation. This was done despite the fact that final agreement on the various conditions of the management contract was not reached until the latter part of 1941.

Labour was not quite such a problem at Crewe as it was at Glasgow, but production at Crewe was held up by an unofficial strike, the ostensible reason for which was that girls had been put on small capstans hitherto operated by boys. These boys were on very simple machines and had had no previous experience, but their transfer was alleged to be a displacement of 'skilled labour', even though no boys had been displaced. The significant fact was that girls were not employed on this kind of work at Derby and the management believed that the real trouble had been engineered from Derby, whose shop stewards were trying to insist that labour conditions at Crewe should be identical to those at Derby. This was obviously out of the question, for, as Hives commented in a minute to Sidgreaves, 'even if we had the desire (which we have not) we could not possibly obtain the skilled labour in the Crewe area'. The management had no alternative but to stand firm. In a letter to Alderman Bott of the Crewe Council, Hives pointed out that the girls were actually more expensive than boys and made it clear that Rolls-Royce 'would not tolerate the factory being dislocated by Trade Union rebels whom the Unions cannot control'. The work was actually more suitable for girls – boys soon became bored with repetitive work – and since the unions would not allow boys over the age of sixteen to be employed as apprentices, the latter were very difficult to obtain and some were already travelling considerable distances to work. It was estimated that 700–800 boys were required at Crewe and all the available labour from Crewe itself had already been absorbed. The management also considered that it was unfair to start so many boys on armament work for which there was no assured future. Another fact of some significance was that the leading member of the strike committee was known to have caused a strike at the Stockport works of the Fairey Company, and was on the Air Ministry 'black list'.

The district committee of the Amalgamated Engineering Union (AEU) endorsed the strike and advised the National Executive of the union to endorse it. 'We claim', they said, 'that it [capstans] is a skilled job at Crewe, no matter what it is elsewhere.' The National Executive refused to give its support, however, and Rolls-Royce declined to accept an offer by Sir Francis Joseph to act as arbitrator, wisely insisting that the normal machinery for the settlement of disputes should be used. On 19 April the men returned to work unconditionally.

Some of the arguments employed by the strikers are not without interest. They claimed that Crewe was the 'home of craftsmanship' and that they did not intend to allow 'dilution'. Or to 'permit the introduction of methods employed in motor car factories'. The action of transferring the boys was categorised as a deliberate and calculated attempt to 'break down agreements with the men by employing semi-skilled labour'. On the whole the customary clichés of industrial dispute were employed but their use shows that once established, in whatever context, human traditions and concepts develop the most powerful resistance to change. When it occurs on a large scale, involving the movement of thousands of human beings, change usually creates stress. This is more acute if the circumstances are novel and the stress will invariably find expression in actions or statements which in themselves are frequently irrational and futile. It is the task of the administrator, as well as the social historian, to discover the real origins and motivation of human conflict, but this requires the skill and capacity to lift the veil which the participants in such conflict tend to throw over their real motivations. As Warner and Low have so clearly demonstrated in their study of the industrial strike, and as Alexander Leighton has shown in his analysis of social stress in the Poston relocation centre for Californian Japanese, these phenomena are seldom satisfactorily explained by the simplistic cause-and-effect relationships assumed by the participants in the dispute. The purely economic, the purely legal, or the purely political explanation of such a pheno-menon as a strike – a breakdown in human co-operation – though interesting and possibly informative in itself, is ingenuous because each by itself neglects so many vitally important factors. If history inevitably compels the neglect of many fascinating bypaths, it is often much the poorer for a rigid, if unavoidable, adherence to the main road. But on such subjects as an industrial strike the historian's conclusions should be regarded as a stimulus to further research rather than as a final explanation.

The Air Ministry tried to devise a 'programme' which would co-ordinate the production of aircraft with that of engines. Whereas enormous pressure had been placed on Rolls-Royce in the late 1930s, as possible war approached, to produce every engine it could, when war actually came, the 'programme' was cut back! As a result, Hives felt obliged to write to Sir Wilfrid Freeman at the Air Ministry:

The 1941 Air Ministry engine programme calls for far less monthly output than the last six months in 1940. The present programme we are working to is considerably below the programme which was submitted to us in March of this year, and it was on the March programme that the Ford factory was planned. Our estimates show that by the end of 1941 we shall have produced 2,000 more Merlin engines than the latest Air Ministry programme and that by September 1942 we shall be 5,000 over the programme ... We are finding that with a standardised product like the Merlin we are exceeding our estimates for output ... We cannot see how the Ford factory which is to duplicate Glasgow fits into the Rolls-Royce aero production programme.

In response, the Air Ministry tried to persuade R.H. Coverley, in charge of the Rotol factory, to become a Director of Engine Production at the Ministry. Needless to say, Hives was horri-fied by the prospect of losing such a key man (Coverley had been Hives's Manager of Manufacturing in the Experimental Department before the war), and said to Freeman:

It is difficult for us to understand what the duties of a DEP entail. If we go by our experience the only discussions we have are on engine programmes which do not mean anything because they are altered every few weeks. We have given up worrying about the programmes, and we have accepted that our problem is to produce as many engines as possible and to watch the aircraft constructors' output to see that we are making the right type of engine.

However, Freeman was insistent that Coverley should join the Ministry as Director of Engine Production. He indicated that though Rolls-Royce might produce all the engines required of them, others were unlikely to do so:

I do not think I am giving away any secret when I say that the cumulative deficiency of Bristol engines by the end of 1941 will exceed 2,500.

'DO NOT REFER ME TO ANOTHER GOVERNMENT DEPARTMENT'

Another factor contributing to the slower build-up of both engine and aircraft output in the early months of 1940 was the concentration of management in organising sub-contract programmes which would take time to yield results. As anyone involved in the production of sophisticated pieces of engineering knows, output cannot be turned on, off and on again like a tap. As it happened, many people were not too alarmed in these early months of the war, when nothing much seemed to be happening. Such complacency was very soon shattered when Hitler's Blitzkrieg began in May 1940.

At Rolls-Royce there was no complacency, merely extreme frustration at the incompetence of the local authorities in both Crewe and Glasgow in providing the housing necessary for the company to build up its labour force. Crewe Council had promised to build 1,000 houses by the end of 1938, but by February 1939 had only given one contract for 100. In May 1939, Hives was so incensed that he threatened to move the whole plant unless something was done. As late as October

1939, T.S. Haldenby was telling the Rt. Hon. Sir Kingsley Wood of the Air Ministry that there was little point in opening up the second part of the factory because there was no accommodation for the 2,500 employees who would work there. There were wrangles between the Council and private builders, who were hampered by restrictions and fearful of the escalating costs of materials. In the end, the Air Ministry was forced to step in and make sure adequate housing was built. In the meantime, billeting was imposed on both Crewe householders and the new employees.

There was a similar situation in Glasgow, and again Rolls-Royce were forced to threaten that they would abandon the operation. Hives, immensely frustrated by the delays and excuses, said:

Please do not refer me to another government department or point out that there is a shortage of building materials. You would be surprised if you knew all the shortages that we have to contend with and overcome.

As late as 12 January 1940, Hives felt compelled to write to Sir Kingsley Wood at the Air Ministry:

I understand that you will shortly be receiving a letter from the Lord Provost of Glasgow, Mr Dollan, on the question of houses in the Glasgow district, and especially in connection with the new Rolls-Royce factory at Hillington.

When the site for the factory was chosen it was on the understanding that schemes were in hand to build a large number of houses in the vicinity of the Works. What has happened is that the factory has gone ahead at an accelerated rate, and the building of houses has stopped altogether.

We have had various meetings with all the local authorities, representatives of the Air Ministry, the Commissioner for Special Areas, and the Department of Health for Scotland, but so far – although there is unanimous agreement to the fact that there are no vacant houses in Glasgow and that there is no possibility of obtaining any houses unless they are built – no decision has been taken.

We anticipate obtaining approximately 90% of the labour in the district, but approximately 10% will hold key positions and we require approximately 1,500 houses.

I am pleased to say that the factory is making very good progress. We have over 1,200 people working for Rolls-Royce at the Hillington factory. We have already started producing a small number of parts for Merlin engines. We have obtained agreement from the Unions to use a very high proportion of female labour, a large number of whom are already being trained.

Where we are going to be stuck is on the housing problem. We have had several cases where key men have been transferred to Glasgow but would not stop, solely on account of not being able to find a house and with no prospect of finding a house.

Lord Provost Dollan knows the position quite well, and I trust that when you receive his proposals some action will be taken.

In retrospect, in view of the desperate situation faced by the country, and considering how close Hitler's forces came to invading, it seems incredible that production of vital war components – and they do not come much more vital than Merlin engines for Spitfires and Hurricanes – should have been held up by strikes.

The situation in Glasgow was just as bad as that already described in Crewe, if not worse. Hives, in response to complaints about quality and scrap rates, said to Major Bulman of the Air Ministry:

We must expect that we shall get criticism in the management of any factory. But any criticism we get from outside cannot possibly approach the criticism we level against ourselves. The district is seething with communists, and strikes and threats of strikes occur the whole time.

William J. (Bill) Miller was put in charge of the operational side of the Glasgow factory, and he too was critical of some of his workforce. He wrote later:

During the first six months of operation at Hillington we took on and trained the machine-operators required for production, but as nearly all fit males had already been called up for war service, only those men who were unfit for the army, or were conscientious objectors, were available for employment. Unfortunately, a large number of the conscientious objectors were Communists and many of them managed, by hook or by crook, to become shop-stewards – with militant attitudes. Many of the shop steward committees were inclined to encourage strike action for the most trivial of reasons. Also, most Clydeside factories called for their machines to be operated only by time-served men, and most of the machines we were using were considered to be skilled-type machines. Because of this, we had to negotiate a special 'relaxation' agreement to allow us to use unskilled labour for both operating and even setting these machines. We were finally successful in getting the sought-after agreement from the unions – but for the duration of the war only.

We have to feel a certain sympathy for the grumbles of the workforce. The hours were punishing, as is made clear by Miller:

After some months at Hillington, with many periods being spent by the employees in underground shelters when the air-raid sirens sounded, absenteeism began to rise considerably due to the workers suffering from physical and mental fatigue, and in a bid to try and resolve the problem we reduced the working hours slightly – i.e. to eighty-two hours a week – by means of arranging one half-Sunday a month as holiday for the work-force.

Female labour predominated and the five years' apprentice-ship, which had been the norm with men before the war, was reduced to *just three weeks*. This did mean an excessive scrap rate for the first six months of the factory's operation but, according to Miller, after eighteen months Hillington was manufacturing every single component of the Merlin and after another twelve months the factory was producing compo-nents for the planned 100 engines a week as well as building and testing the engines. By then they were also repairing engines that were coming in after 240 flying hours in the Battle of

Britain. Furthermore, the engines being built at Packard in the USA were being sent to Hillington for modification before they went into service.

By the end of 1940 Rolls-Royce in Glasgow was employing no fewer than 26,000 and the company was using a former WD and HO Wills (cigarette manufacturers) factory in Alexandra Parade, Glasgow, and a small empty lace factory at Thornliebank in addition to the plant at Hillington.

In spite of all the problems, the first complete engine came out of the Glasgow factory in November 1940, and even before then Crewe and Derby output had benefited from parts supplied from Glasgow. By June 1941 the target of 200 engines per month was reached, and by March 1942 output exceeded 400 per month.

Hives's workload during the immediate pre-war years and, of course, during the war itself was monumental. Bill Miller in his memoirs gives some idea of his commitments:

The purpose of the new Hillington factory was to manufacture Merlin engines for the Spitfire and Hurricane fighter planes and the Lancaster bombers being used by the Royal Air Force. Mr Hives made each of us managers directly responsible to himself, but as he was running the Derby and Crewe factories, plus the entire engineering department, and also had to attend War Cabinet meetings every Wednesday in London, he was able to spend at the most only one day a week with us at Glasgow.

The trip to Glasgow was not a one-hour flight as it would be now but either a long motor car journey or, worse, a long train journey with the interminable delays which are one of the abiding memories of those forced to travel in the war years. Bill Miller gives some idea of the travelling conditions in winter:

Only a few main roads were being regularly gritted and sanded, and most of the other roads became repeatedly covered with snow, which frequently turned to ice which in turn melted then re-froze, and so on, until even the Hillington Road began to suffer from numerous pot-holes measuring six to nine inches in depth.

Alec Harvey-Bailey in his book *Rolls-Royce – Hives, the Quiet Tiger*, published by the Rolls-Royce Heritage Trust, also wrote of Hives's workload:

There was no phoney war in Rolls-Royce. Crewe now had 3,000 on the strength and Hives was making weekly trips to Glasgow to progress the factory. Glasgow was an Air Ministry factory, for which Rolls-Royce had a management contract, and he found this to be more difficult administratively than Crewe, which worked as an extension of Derby. These visits continued throughout the war and in 1940 he had 3-B-50 fitted with long range tanks so that in an emergency he could make the round trip to Glasgow and back without refuelling, but more generally he went by sleeper. It was his standard practice to go straight from the station to his office on his return to Derby. Every Monday was the Hives meeting, when he reviewed the engineering programme on the Merlin, which included the six worst service troubles. Monthly he met the unions at the JPC meeting. On many evenings he had visitors at Duffield Bank House, which were working sessions, apart from a few frames of snooker after dinner, which was a ritual with him and woebetide those who were no good.

FORD AS WELL

The Air Ministry decided in November 1939 that the combined output of Rolls-Royce Derby and the two shadow factories in Crewe and Glasgow would still not produce the quantity of Merlins likely to be required. Sir Wilfrid Freeman sent for Rowland (later Sir Rowland) Smith, Managing Director of Ford in the UK, and asked him if Ford would be prepared to manufacture Merlin engines.

Rowland Smith said that they would and asked how many the Air Ministry would want. The answer was 400 a month. Smith said that could be done and the Ford and Air Ministry teams set about organising the project. Major Bulman recalled:

Smith was a great man in every sense, and realised that his team must steep themselves in all the know-how of building aero-engines as distinct from Ford cars. With the complete support of Hives, he therefore sent ninety of his best men to Derby for training and they were there for nine months. The Ford estimate of production cost was £5 million [£250 million in today's terms], and it was Freeman's view that the matter was so urgent that he side-stepped the usual official approval process and sent me to the Treasury to get the necessary authority, and incredible though it seems, I received it within five minutes due to the perception of our administrative Civil Servants of those days. Smith decided to build an entirely new factory at Trafford Park, outside Manchester, compromising on the true Ford method of production in order to begin delivery in June 1940 rather than his initially estimated two and a half years. The result was a machine shop containing single-purpose tools tailored to the Merlin's design, though less capable of being switched to the different engines, fundamentally far more productive of Merlins than the Rolls-Royce line, and making a cheaper engine of no less superb quality.

The teams had decided that it would be a mistake to try to impose the extra production on Ford's Dagenham plant, which was already engaged in vital war work. After inspecting eight possible sites they selected a site on the Trafford Park Industrial Estate in Manchester where the first Ford car assembly plant in the UK had been erected in 1911.

How would Ford cope? Harold Nockolds explained in his *The Magic of a Name*:

The reader may well ask how the requisite number of skilled workers could be found to be entrusted with the manufacture of such vast quantities of complex aero-engines to the exacting Rolls-Royce standards and precision, not only at Trafford Park, but at Crewe and Glasgow, too. Several things made this possible. In the first place, in the years before the war there had been a tremendous development of automatic and semi-automatic machine tools which can turn out large numbers of intricate parts with a high degree of accuracy. Secondly, these machines can be worked by trainees and unskilled operatives.

What was wanted was a nucleus of skilled men who could not

merely operate such machine tools, but could set them up according to drawings and adjust them to keep producing accurate 'bits and pieces'.

It is fair to say that the Derby factory had a uniquely high proportion of these skilled workers, who had started as apprentices, and this explains why Rolls-Royce were able to operate the new factories at Crewe and Glasgow without assistance. All they did was to take skilled men from Derby and promote them to positions of responsibility. The company's policy of 'investing in talent', as Hives describes it, paid handsome dividends to the national cause during the war, and he insists that the vast expansion of output was achieved not so much by building factories as by Rolls-Royce having sufficient skilled men with the requisite 'know how'. But there was a limit to this process, and when the Ford project arose, there were insufficient skilled men left at Derby to provide the necessary nucleus for Trafford Park.

Hives and Rowland Smith got over this difficulty by starting a miniature factory in a building at Derby, where 190 of Fords' best men were given the 20,000 drawings of the Merlin and told to set up their machines to produce the 10,000 separate parts of the engine. The men were moved on from machine to machine until each man had built a complete Merlin. They were then ready to start production at Trafford Park, using unskilled labour to look after the machines they had set up.

Another reason why the precise engineering required to make Rolls-Royce aero-engines was no longer entirely a closed book was the elaborate system of inspection employed in the Rolls-Royce technique. The purpose of this inspection (which was performed after each operation) was not only to maintain the standard of quality but also to avoid working on parts which would be subsequently found below par. In the whole Rolls-Royce wartime organisation there were over 5,000 inspectors, comprising nearly one-tenth of the total staff, and it was only to be expected that the proportion was much higher at Crewe and Glasgow, where most of the workers were new to the job and therefore 'unskilled', than at Derby.

The Ford project was so successful that by the end of the war the total output of Trafford Park reached 30,000 engines. The factory employed 17,316 workers, of whom 7,200 were women. In the Rolls-Royce factories women formed nearly one-third of the total workers.

Nockolds glossed over the difficulties involved. However, in his book *Not much of an Engineer*, Sir Stanley Hooker wrote:

One day their Chief Engineer appeared in Lovesey's office, which I was then sharing, and said, 'you know we can't make the Merlin to these drawings.'

I replied loftily, 'I suppose that is because the drawing tolerances are too difficult for you, and you can't achieve the accuracy.'

'On the contrary', he replied, 'the tolerances are far too wide for us. We make motor cars far more accurately than this. Every part on our car engines has to be interchangeable with the same part on any other engine, and hence all parts have to be made with extreme accuracy, far closer than you use. That is the only way we can achieve mass production.'

Lovesey joined in. 'Well, what do you propose now?'

The reply was that Ford would have to redraw all of the Merlin drawings to their own standards, and this they did. It took a year or so, but was an enormous success, because, once the great Ford factory at Manchester started production, Merlins came out like shelling peas at the rate of 400 a week. And very good engines they were too, yet never have I seen mention of this massive contribution which the British Ford company made to the build-up of our air forces.

CHAPTER FOUR

A MAGNIFICENT EXAMPLE OF ANGLO-AMERICAN CO-OPERATION

NO MERLINS FOR FRANCE
'GO TO WASHINGTON AND DELIVER THE ROLLS-ROYCE PLANS'
FORD OR PACKARD?
SIXTY THOUSAND GAUGES, TOOLS AND FIXTURES

NO MERLINS FOR FRANCE

When Rolls-Royce had moved from small production of specialist luxury cars to heavy production of aero engines it was inevitable they would become involved with mass producers. The biggest company they dealt with in France, the UK and then the USA was the Ford Motor Company, founded by Henry Ford in 1896 and generally regarded as the pioneer of mass production. We all know his famous saying, 'Tell him he can have any colour he likes so long as it's black.'

In 1939 the French aero engine industry was unable to meet the demand for engines from its own airframe manufacturers. In view of the world-wide reputation which Merlin was rapidly acquiring for its performance in the Hurricane and Spitfire, the French Air Ministry decided to request Monsieur Dollfuss, Managing Director of the firm of Fordair, a subsidiary of the American Ford Company in France, to negotiate with Rolls-Royce for a licence to manufacture the Merlin. The original scheme was discussed in London in March 1939, and was not very ambitious. Monsieur Dollfuss pointed out confidentially to Colonel Darby, an experienced executive entrusted with the negotiations with the French Government, that his company was not really interested in making complete engines for some time. His intention was to work with Rolls-Royce 'on a basis of assembly'. During the course of discussions with Colonel Darby he put forward the view that the whole proposal had been made 'purely from the point of view of satisfying political opinion in France'. In view of subsequent developments, these statements seem to have been particularly frank and prophetic.

But though the Rolls-Royce management would probably never have considered such a proposal had it been made after the outbreak of war, it must be remembered that in March 1939 an intelligent commercial policy had at least to cover the possibility that war would not break out. Under these circumstances an opportunity to increase the income to be obtained from the licence and subsequent manufacture of the company's products abroad could not be neglected.

The British Air Ministry, which was kept informed of the trend of these discussions throughout, agreed to the sale of manufacturing rights on certain conditions. The first of these was that the early Mark III Merlins could be released in connection with the contract and the building up of production in France, but not the late Merlin Xs. It was realised that there was no hope of the Fordair factory producing complete Merlins for the French aircraft manufacturers much before the spring of 1940, and in consequence in the initial stages the Amiot and Dewoitine French aircraft factories were to be dependent almost completely on Derby. At this stage the Fordair project was regarded by the French more as a scheme for providing repair, overhaul and test facilities for Merlins supplied from Derby. The project was regarded at Derby as a purely commercial transaction, and the prices quoted were commercial prices – up to 100 at £3,300, up to 200 at £3,200 and over 200 at £3,100 (to arrive at today's prices multiply by 50 so £165,000, £160,000 and £155,000). The manufacturing licence was sold directly to the French Government for £50,000 and on top of this there was a royalty of £200 per engine which would be proportionately reduced by the value of British-made parts in any complete engines assembled in France in the early stages. Similar conditions governed the production of spare parts. A clause in the contract which later gave rise to considerable misunderstanding entitled the French Government to negotiate a licence on similar terms for any future engines which Rolls-Royce might develop. The licence was sub-licensed to Fordair. The British Air Ministry laid down two further conditions. The first of these required Rolls-Royce to 'provide reciprocal information as regards design, maintenance, installation and other technical experience between yourselves and your licensee'. Any information received in this way was to be made available to the Air Ministry. The second condition was that Rolls-Royce would pay to the Air Ministry a proportion of the royalty payments. Both these conditions were agreed to by Rolls-Royce.

Before the final details of the agreement had been completed a number of Ford engineers arrived at Derby to gain a general idea of the manufacturing techniques involved in Merlin production. Some of these men were from the parent company in Detroit and had worked on the Liberty project in the First World War. These engineers were given full run of the Derby factory and spent about six months there. Most of the information was passed back to Detroit, where the parent company was carrying out the production planning of the entire scheme. The special machine tools, none of which were obtainable in France, were all ordered and progressed from the Dearborn headquarters of the Ford Company in Detroit.

Production was planned to start at the Ford Strasbourg plant while a new factory at Bordeaux was being completed. The original scheme envisaged the production of parts in four stages. Output was expected to reach a figure of fifteen engines per week at the Bordeaux factory.

Fordair's contact with Derby was thus of a very indirect nature and, though Rolls-Royce more than fulfilled the letter and spirit of the contract in the supply of blueprints and technical knowledge, very little progress was made in the few remaining months before the outbreak of war. Fords at Detroit

9. Hives – solid, dependable, decisive, an inspiration
to all who worked with him.

10. Griffon engine parts laid out for inspection after testing in the Experimental Department in Derby in 1943.

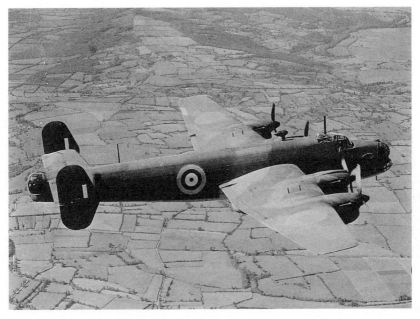

11. A Merlin-powered Handley Page Halifax
heavy bomber.

12. The end of a shift at the Derby works.

13. Merlin-powered Hurricanes in September 1939 around
the time of the outbreak of the war.

14. The Rolls-Royce works in Hillington, Glasgow.
Hives went there every week and it did not take only an hour
in those days but many hours either by road or by train.

15. A Merlin-powered Avro Lancaster bomber.

16. Hives with Jesse G. Vincent, Vice-President Engineering at Packard, the company which made the Merlin under licence in the USA.

had at one stage considered using the tools of the Lincoln automobile plant for Merlin production, but this was quickly abandoned when some of the Rolls-Royce engineers who saw it pointed out its general unsuitability. In other respects, however, the planning work done at Detroit was very thorough – although Fords, through pressure on their own facilities, sub-contracted most of the work.

The project did not fare so well in its execution in France. As early as July it appeared most unlikely that the French factories would be able to build anything approaching an assembly line from their own parts. There was a severe short-age of jigs and tools (which were in short supply everywhere as a result of rearmament) and of specialised draughtsmen. In consequence it was decided that Rolls-Royce could best assist the project by supplying sets of almost complete engines which could be assembled in France. On 24 July Sir Wilfrid Freeman agreed to recommend to the Air Council a pro-gramme for the delivery of 75 sets of Merlin parts between September 1939 and January 1940. This was to be followed by a further 100 sets up until May 1940, and a further 50 between the end of May and August. It was expected that deliveries would begin early in 1940 and it was stipulated in the agreement that 125 of the first 250 engines would be returned to the Air Ministry. The Air Ministry was not prepared to forgo more than 125 engines at this stage, but the figure of 250 was agreed to help the French factory to achieve more continuous production.

On 21 August there was a completely unexpected develop-ment at Dearborn. Henry Ford, who was not impressed by Britain's or France's chances of defeating a sustained German attack, decided to keep his American plants strictly neutral. As a result of this decision all Merlin and other armament work of any description was rapidly cleared out of the Ford factories and organisation at Detroit. Work on the special machine tools for the Bordeaux factory was suspended, and though the orders for machine tools were not actually cancelled their makers were left uncertain as to their ultimate fate. All the American engineers in France were recalled to the

United States. The situation was further complicated by the uncertainties and intricacies of the Neutrality Act.

The effect of all this on the French project was shattering. It soon became apparent that the French organisation and management had relied very heavily on the Detroit firm. In a report written on 12 December the two Rolls-Royce representatives at Bordeaux, Willis and Buxton, made the following pertinent observation:

This Company in the past, in the production of Ford cars, have had all the construction and organising work done for them by the American parent concern, who have prepared all designs of highly specialised plant and tools and have managed the planning and starting of plant here, leaving only the maintenance work to be done by themselves, with the result that the organisation here do not appear to know how to start on their own initiative without outside help to start the plant for them.

To complicate matters even further the French Government ordered the removal of the entire Strasbourg staff and movable plant to Bordeaux. The Bordeaux factory had been very fully equipped with standard machine tools and was almost ready to start production but most of the staff at Bordeaux were called up on the outbreak of war. The chaotic state of the administration, the remaining members of which were working 60 hours a week in an endeavour to get the factory running, the virtual cancellation of the special machines on order in the United States, and the fact, discovered by Rolls-Royce just before the outbreak of war, that the French factory intended to rely completely on the United States for supplies of raw materials, together presented a depressing picture.

A conference on the subject was called in London on 12 September at which M. Dollfuss, M. Ricardo of the French Air Ministry and M. Panier of Fords were present. At this meeting Dollfuss explained what had happened in France and suggested that the French factory should now act as sub-contractors to Derby. For them to be able to do this, however, Rolls-Royce would have to provide the essential machine tools, and it was equally obvious that technical assistance would also have to be provided on a much greater scale than that contemplated in the original agreement. If Rolls-Royce was unable to provide this assistance, Dollfuss pointed out, the French factory would have to be employed in the manufacture of Hispano-Suiza engines. Hives did not intend to be saddled with the additional burden of getting the French factory into production. He suggested that Rolls-Royce would provide whatever assistance was within their power but that they could not be expected to tool up the French factory. He saw no reason why the tools should not still be obtained from the United States. The question of quantities was raised and Dollfuss pointed out that the French Government had, since the outbreak of the war, doubled its original order for 1,250 Merlins plus 30 per cent spares. This meant that the Bordeaux factory was required to plan for a production of twelve engines per day. It was generally agreed at the meeting that the idea of producing complete engines was somewhat too ambitious in view of the complications which had developed, and that the best plan was for Derby to continue with the scheme to provide the French factory with sets of parts in an endeavour to build up production by stages. The idea was that the French factory would supply both parts and the complete engines assembled from the parts supplied from Derby and Fordair direct to England. The complete engines would be tested at Derby and supplied to the French Government direct.

On 21 September Colonel Darby left for France to survey the whole organisation and report on the progress which had been made. Rolls-Royce had agreed to offer all possible help within reason on the condition that the French management took the main burden of the responsibility for getting production started. A peculiar feature of the situation was the lack of liaison between the French and the English Ford Company at Dagenham. The latter had been asking the Air Ministry for work and Rolls-Royce could not understand why the French company did not seek their help. Before he left for France Colonel Darby contacted the Dagenham factory, discovered that they had tool capacity available, and cabled this information to Dollfuss.

Hives was very sceptical about the whole project and on 25 September he expressed serious doubts to Sir Wilfrid Freeman:

My own views are that the French company are just playing with the job; in fact I even doubt their honesty of purpose. The impression I have is that they have been given huge orders by the French Air Ministry for Ford trucks and they certainly have not the capacity to tackle the Merlin job unless it operates an entirely separate division. The promises which the French Ford Company made to the French Air Ministry to produce Merlin engines and parts were just ridiculous. It either meant they were thoroughly dishonest or that they had not grasped in any way the magnitude of the job they had undertaken.

A further meeting with the directors of the French company and representatives of the French Air Ministry was held in Derby on 6 October. Hives was critical of the way in which the entire project was being handled and alleged that the French company had made no serious effort to get into production. He was opposed to the suggestion that the French company should manufacture so-called 'bottle-neck' items, since the labels on the bottles were constantly varying and this did not provide a firm basis for an intelligent production plan. He was of the opinion that the French factory should still aim at the production of complete engines. If they planned to produce engines as soon as possible there was a possibility that they would at least produce parts. The American machine tools had been released by this time, which made this quite a feasible proposition and one which set the French management a clear and unequivocal target.

A major objection raised by Monsieur Dollfuss to this proposal was that the capital of the French company (£1,600,000) was not large enough to finance the production of complete engines. He also complained that Rolls-Royce were not giving the French organisation the technical assistance which they had expected and which he considered to be implied in the contract. These recriminations were not helpful and the conference achieved very little. Hives was very dissatisfied and in a report to the board he reverted to the point of view that the most that could be expected of the French factory was assistance in the assembly of a small number of engines and in the production of scheduled parts for which they had the equipment.

The accusation that Rolls-Royce have not been helpful is entirely untrue; in fact I will go so far as to say that our enthusiasm to help may have lulled Fordair into thinking that there was very little for them to do ... There have been endless discussions as regards the position of the plant and machinery in France, but the fact which stands out is that although these negotiations started last March, today there is not a single machine available in France ready to produce Merlin pieces ... Technical information is not a commodity which you can wrap up in a parcel and deliver, it can only be of value when it is conveyed to a person who understands and desires the knowledge ... Fordair have not grasped this fundamental point.

On 6 November H.J. Swift left for France and spent a week at the Fordair factory. His report, which was not entirely unfavourable and did not underrate the great efforts which had been made by some of the Fordair engineers, supported Hives's view that there was no clear objective and that the French management had greatly underestimated the complexity of aero engine production.

Two factories were in operation at Bordeaux. The new plant was not ready to start production when the move from Strasbourg took place and in consequence a small plant at Poissy, just nearby, had been started on the production of tools. This factory, which was well designed and intended to employ 6,000 men in an area of 480,000 square feet, was only 60 per cent complete and employing only 600 men. There were no Fellowes gear-cutting machines and Swift did not expect the factory to produce a complete engine until September 1940 at the earliest. 'It seems obvious', he wrote, 'from the nebulous state in both factories and from the machine tools and the small amount of skilled labour available that it is not likely that there will be any extensive production of components from France for a very long time to come.' A most serious problem was the 'crippling lack of skilled designers and toolmakers', and Swift concluded that until the American effort began to materialise very little could be expected from the factory.

The Rolls-Royce representative at Bordeaux confirmed Swift's opinion that it would be a long time before the factory turned out a compete Merlin, though he attributed this to the mass-production mentality.

I am favourably impressed with the ability of the men I have met here. Their chief difficulty will be the enlistment of skilled men to assist them in the great effort they have undertaken … They only think along the lines of Ford mass-production and in consequence they will not start producing till every gauge, tool and cotter pin is ready and at hand … I am afraid it will be some time before a complete unit is off test and ready for delivery.

Willis was very critical of the poor managerial organisation. There was little positive control and no one would take responsibility. The course of these negotiations throws a very revealing light on the general state of the French aircraft industry in 1939. The position at the aircraft firms, which several Rolls-Royce representatives visited in the course of supervising the installation of Merlins in various production and prototype aircraft, was little better. By comparison, the picture in Britain was one of superlative organisation and efficiency.

The project was not heartily backed by the French Air Ministry, which always gave the impression of wanting to obtain something for nothing and adopted an indignant attitude when it was pointed out that the results would depend very largely on their own efforts. It is apparent that there was a great deal of politics involved on the French side and that the final cancellation of the manufacturing project on 18 December was the result of high-level intrigue in French military, political and commercial circles. The French, in 1940, clearly preferred politics to production.

On 9 December Monsieur Dollfuss wrote to Sidgreaves informing him that Rolls-Royce had not, in Fordair's opinion, fulfilled their obligations under the agreement: 'As I led you to anticipate at our last conference in Derby, the assistance which you were able to give us as regards assembly, tests and supplies of finished parts was judged inadequate by the French Air Ministry to ensure, together with our production, a sufficient output of Merlin X motors.' He informed Sidgreaves that the French Air Ministry intended to fulfil the other clauses of the contract and that Rolls-Royce would be expected to fulfil all other orders. The letter concluded with a peremptory demand that Rolls-Royce should make available to the French Air Ministry the plans of all engines then under development. The licence had in fact contained an option, exercisable within five years, to produce new engines which Rolls-Royce put into production at Derby, the terms and conditions of production being subject to negotiation. Dollfuss's letter, which did not reach England until 28 December, ten days after the cancellation of the licence but clearly anticipating it, was an ineffective *tour de force* and an attempt to cover up the fact that the French had decided to produce the Hispano-Suiza engine at Bordeaux because the Merlin had proved beyond the capacity of the Fordair organisation.

Rolls-Royce did not in the least regret the loss of this commitment, which had absorbed an excessive amount of the valuable time of the company's senior officials and had achieved nothing. In a letter informing Maurice Olley of what had happened Hives said that he considered it to be 'the best thing that could have happened both as regards providing the maximum war effort and also to relieve us of one of our worries'. Even payment of the quite clear-cut financial obligations of the French Government under the licence involved tedious negotiation and delay.

Though the project for manufacturing Merlins in France was completely abandoned, the French Air Force still required Merlin engines for two types of aircraft – the Amiot bomber and Dewoitine fighter – which it was intended should use them. By 11 April, 126 engines had actually been delivered under the agreement between the British and French Air Ministries, and it appeared that the French intended to ask for another 200 engines when the 300 originally ordered had been delivered. By the fall of France, 143 Merlins had been delivered in all. This figure was substantially below that which the French Government had hoped for, but in view of subsequent events, and the fact that the aircraft firms seemed incapable of putting their aircraft into the air, it was in France's own interests that the remaining Merlins should remain in England to reinforce the strength of the RAF. From many points of view it is just as well that the resources of the Rolls-Royce management were not diverted, as they might easily have been, into building up a substantial and reliable unit for Merlin manufacture in France. This could have been done only at the expense of Derby, Crewe and Glasgow, and had it been successful the Germans would have been presented with a first-class organisation which they would not have hesitated to use. Nor could it be argued, in view of the facts presented above, that, had the scheme matured more rapidly, this would have greatly increased the strength of the French Air Force. Such an achievement would have required a great deal more than the successful reorganisation of one factory.

'GO TO WASHINGTON AND DELIVER THE ROLLS-ROYCE PLANS'

Hives realised by the middle of 1940 that, despite the super-human efforts he and his teams were making, they were not capable of meeting the demands made of them by the Air Ministry. In June the group was asked to produce 3,636 Merlins of all marks between August and December, and 5,995 in the first six months of 1941. In July these figures were stepped up to 3,639 and 6,096 and in September to 3,899 and 6,983. At the same time the Vulture and Kestrel requirements were increased. The first figure was not excessively optimistic, the output achieved from all factories in the last five months of 1940 being 3,515. But the expectations for the first six months of 1941 were far too optimistic, the output actually achieved in this period being only 4,710 engines.

In view of these expectations Hives thought it expedient to raise the question of parts manufacture in the United States. Beaverbrook had his own ideas on this subject and on 28 May intervened in a drastic manner. Instructions were telephoned to Derby that a complete set of Merlin and Griffon blueprints were to be prepared for immediate transhipment to the United States. Similar instructions were also received by several other firms. This was done and the prints were collected by special train and delivered to a warship which was leaving for Canada. On 12 June Mr M.W. Wilson, the President of the Royal Bank of Canada, received the following instructions from Lord Beaverbrook. 'Please go to Washington and deliver the Rolls-Royce and Handley-Page plans to the President forthwith, intimating that you are handing them over upon my official authority and instructions with a view to their immediate use for the production of aircraft engines and frames. The rights of Rolls-Royce and Handley-Page can be left for subsequent determination and adjustment between the two countries.' A copy of these instructions was received at Derby.

As soon as this news was received at Derby, Sidgreaves gave instructions for the order to be carried out and then drafted a letter to the Minister in which he pointed out that the board was disturbed by his action. 'Whilst they appreciate that the present is not the right time to raise financial questions, nevertheless as custodians of the assets which belong to the shareholders of the Company, they feel that it is desirable to place on record the fact that in carrying out these instructions they are parting with a very valuable asset.' This letter was not sent and instead Sidgreaves and Hives requested and obtained an interview. At this meeting Lord Beaverbrook pointed out that the whole question of Merlin manufacture in the United States was under discussion at the Ministry and gave an assurance that the legitimate commercial claims of the company would not be ignored. 'Under these circumstances', he wrote a few days later, 'I would ask you to be good enough to refrain from entering into any negotiations with the American Government and to advise your American representatives accordingly.'

The Chairman, Lord Herbert Scott, was extremely concerned at this high-handed action by Beaverbrook.

Such action would place our shareholders in an impossible position ... Knowing something about Beaverbrook's methods he would be unscrupulous to gain a point considered to be in our national interest. If, for instance, he could barter Merlins with the United States, for, say, ships, guns, munitions etc, he would not hesitate to do so without any reference to ourselves or regard to our shareholders.

Scott had been a director of Rolls-Royce Limited since 1906, and had already witnessed Beaverbrook's methods when Beaverbrook bought Charles Rolls's shares after his death in 1910. Managing Director Arthur Sidgreaves was more sanguine:

By the time America can produce any Merlins, the engine as a type will be out of date here. Quite frankly our feeling (I think we can include Hives) is that if their having the drawings would enable us to win the war we would willingly give them without any claim. If we lose the war it certainly won't matter about the drawings.

Sidgreaves will almost certainly have been party to Churchill's attempts to persuade the USA to back Britain's war effort. A study given to the War Cabinet in May 1940 under the title 'British Strategy in a Certain Eventuality' said, according to Hancock and Gowing in their book *British War Economy*, that 'they ruled out submission but saw no chance of final victory unless full economic support was forthcoming from the United States'.

Rolls-Royce had looked at the possibility of having Merlins made in the USA before the outbreak of war, as is made clear in this memo to Sidgreaves from Hives on 12 October 1938:

We have had from time to time various enquiries as to whether we would contemplate granting a licence to manufacture our aero-engines in America. They have come from finance people and some from aircraft constructors ... I suggest it is very important that the licence should only be given to some organisation that has already established an engineering background.

You will remember when the Pratt & Whitney people came into the engine business they had previously been machine tool manufacturers and as a result had the right mentality and have made a great success.

The following month, Sidgreaves sent a memo to Hives about another possible licensee who was interested – Packard. He wrote, 'This of course sounds pretty good as we know that Packard's are a reliable engineering firm to whom we could entrust the job.'

Hives was more sanguine about production in the USA than either Scott or Sidgreaves. As soon as war had broken out Hives had raised the question of production in the United States. In a letter to Sir Wilfrid Freeman he advocated the production of selected parts which were likely to prove difficult items in Britain and for which the creation of additional capacity would have been either impossible or excessively costly in Britain. He considered that a carefully constructed programme of this type would achieve, for a given expenditure of dollars, a far greater increase in production than that which the import of an equivalent value of machine tools would make possible. There were two other factors of considerable importance. The Ford Company at Detroit had already received, and had been working on, a complete set of Merlin drawings on behalf of their subsidiary in France and had placed large orders for machine tools. It thus seemed logical that if any company should produce the Merlin in the United States it should be the Ford Company, but for various reasons which will be discussed later, this did not take place. The second point which Hives rightly stressed was that most of the machine tool equipment for the production of the difficult pieces of the Merlin was already obtained from the

United States. A large amount of equipment had been ordered for Crewe and Glasgow and he suggested that it might be wiser to leave this in the United States where there was an abundance of skilled labour and little risk of enemy action. This argument was strongly supported by the fact that soon after the outbreak of war two ships carrying machine tools for Rolls-Royce, the S.S. *Malabar* and the S.S. *City of Flint*, were torpedoed and sunk. But the optimum utilisation of British-owned resources in the United States was clearly a matter of high-level state priority and many of the problems involved had hardly been discussed at this stage. Hives concluded by stressing the need for speed. 'In the last war it took us two years before we appreciated the possibility of producing aero-engines in the United States. This time, if we mean business, whatever we can possibly do out there should be done as quickly as possible.'

At the same time, Hives wanted Beaverbrook to be aware of the enormity of the task of ensuring that Merlin engines produced in another country over 3,000 miles away were up to the standard required. He consequently wrote to Beaverbrook on 8 July 1940:

The three Rolls-Royce Engineers who you have agreed should go to the USA in order to assist in the production of Rolls-Royce engines or parts have now received the official information that they will be enrolled on the Ministry of Aircraft Production Staff in the USA, working in conjunction with Rolls-Royce.

When Mr Sidgreaves and I see you on Wednesday afternoon, we are very anxious to clear up the question of how you expect them to operate. We are positive that any project for producing Rolls-Royce engines or parts in the USA can only be successful with the full co-operation and experience of Rolls-Royce help. THE FACT THAT MERLIN DRAWINGS HAVE BEEN SENT TO THE USA DOES NOT MEAN THAT THEY ARE IN A POSITION TO PRODUCE MERLIN ENGINES. [authors' capitals]

The proposal to manufacture Merlins in the United States soon received considerable publicity in both countries. In the meantime, however, the Rolls-Royce representatives in the United States had been active in the organisation of parts, raw material and machine tool supplies. An efficient and comprehensive organisation under the control of J. McManus and Maurice Olley was set up with offices in Michigan and New York. Hives was all in favour of expanding this organisation into a great sub-contract scheme similar to that existing in Britain. 'I can promise you', he told the Minister, 'that you would get an infinitely better return for your money by making full use of sub-contracting in the USA and Canada to produce Merlin pieces than you will by the Ford Company attempting to make complete engines at £5,000 each.'

The question of an American Merlin licence had been raised several times even before the war by manufacturers in the United States, who had approached either McManus in New York or Colonel Darby in London. In October 1938 several enquiries had been received in London from American manufacturers who considered that the development of military aircraft in the United States was hampered by the lack of liquid-cooled engines. These manufacturers had also made representations to the American Government and Colonel Darby thought that it was an opportune time to arrange a licence. Sidgreaves and Hives did not agree. 'If the American Government,' wrote Sidgreaves, 'as a result of their investigations overseas, come to the conclusion that they want Rolls-Royce engines, then I would much rather they approached us than vice versa.' In November one of the directors of the Packard Company who was visiting London discussed the possibility of a licence with Colonel Darby, but nothing further came of the proposal for very much the same reasons.

After war broke out Sidgreaves wrote to McManus pointing out that Rolls-Royce was less interested than ever in granting a licence since the firm's whole effort would be fully absorbed in England. But, despite this cold water poured on every suggestion that complete engines should be made in America, McManus and Olley continued to discuss the possibility with various manufacturers who were interested in the idea. In October 1938 Olley had met the General Manager of

Packards, Mr G.T. Christopher, who told him that his company was thinking of returning to the aero engine business and suggested forming with Rolls-Royce in the United States a company similar in character to Rotols. In this event Packards would be prepared to release a proportion of their manufacturing facilities for the manufacture of Rolls-Royce products generally.

In discussing this proposal Olley could not resist a sarcastic comment on the previous organisation which Rolls-Royce had established in Springfield, Mass. after the First World War. The new company, he declared, 'would not have in it investment bankers and their stock profits, watered stock, operation from Wall Street, with overpaid officials sitting around waiting for a factory to be equipped and lined up, plus high-paid officials for selling and palatial showrooms to sit in and not sell'. Sidgreaves was neither impressed by the proposal nor stung by the sarcasm. 'In reality when we get down to it', he replied, 'we find that there are a lot of people who want to make Rolls-Royce engines, repair them and everything else so long as Rolls-Royce will do all the work.' Despite the disappointment of the Fordair project, which no doubt prompted this remark, he thought that the Ford Company would be the best equipped to undertake Merlin manufacture in the United States because of the work which their engineers had already done on behalf of their French subsidiary.

FORD OR PACKARD?

A further meeting between Maurice Olley and the Chairman of the Packard Company, Mr Gilman, took place early in December. Mr Gilman's attitude was quite co-operative, as Olley pointed out to Mr Purvis, one of the officials on the British Purchasing Commission in Washington. Gilman was ready at any time, he said, 'to put the Packard organisation to work on building Merlin engines for the Air Ministry. He is not prepared to risk the Packard Company's capital on the job, nor is he willing to sign a standard licensing agreement with Rolls-Royce or the Air Ministry which would involve the expenditure of large amounts of Packard capital without assurance of a return.'

The Packard Company wished the Air Ministry to provide all the capital as it had done for Crewe and Glasgow, and insisted on adequate protection against the financial loss which a sudden cessation of hostilities would have caused, plus a profit of 'between 10 and 15%'. Gilman fully expected that the cost of manufacture in the United States would be double that in England. He did not object to paying Rolls-Royce a royalty since this would merely be added to the cost of the engines. The Packard Company would not accept an order for less than 1,000 engines and could not promise to make delivery before the end of 1940. Gilman frankly doubted if the Air Ministry would consider a proposition of this nature, especially in view of the fact that they had rejected a similar offer from his company in 1938.

In the autumn of 1939 the English management considered that its American representatives had an exaggerated idea of the importance of developing a geographically separate source of supply for complete engines. There is no doubt that the project of manufacturing complete engines in the United States had a much stronger appeal than the more mundane but, from the point of view of British production, more immediately productive scheme for parts manufacture. McManus in particular had always nurtured an ambition to redress the failure of Springfield and there is little doubt that he saw an opportunity of doing so in the American Merlin idea. Early in December S.E. Blackstone, who had gone over at Hives's request to provide Olley and McManus with an up-to-date picture of the requirements of the British factories, especially in machine tools for Crewe and Glasgow, reported back that both of them were disappointed that the British Government was not going ahead. It was not easy, he said, to satisfy them 'that there were no urgent requirements for parts beyond a few which were considered to be vulnerable to air attack, and that our job at present is merely exploratory, to find potential sources for some of the major items such as steels, aluminium castings and forgings, machining larger parts etc.' Maurice

Olley, whose 1914–18 experiences in the United States were still very vivid, was convinced that a complete Merlin would have to be manufactured sooner or later. He had a poor opinion of the only other liquid-cooled in-line engine then being manufactured in America, and considered that though other engines were under development they would be unlikely to appear in time, or to be superior to the Merlin when they did.

The reasons for the English management's continued opposition to the idea were not substantial. In a memorandum to McManus, Sidgreaves summarised the main argument.

On the question of going further with Packard the position is really quite definite that I am not interested in forming any more companies. If Packard wants to make Rolls-Royce engines the only way will be for Packard to build our machines under licence and for the necessary personnel to come over here to study the job from A to Z so that they can go back to America fully equipped with all the information to enable them to produce ... We cannot spare any more personnel for technical educational purposes.

This reply clearly showed that there was no immediate prospect of building complete Merlins in the United States on the company's own initiative, but even this did not extinguish the enthusiasm of the Rolls-Royce representatives in the USA. Both continued to discuss various proposals with industrialists and with the senior technical officials of the US Army Air Force and the US Navy. On 2 March McManus cabled a request that Derby should supply the US War Department with two Merlin engines of the latest type. This request emerged from a visit which he and Olley had paid to Brigadier-General G.H. Brett and Rear-Admiral Towers at Washington in an attempt to interest the United States service chiefs directly in the Merlin as an engine for American fighter aircraft. The performance of American fighter aircraft in 1939 was notoriously inferior to that of the aircraft of the major European powers. But before the Army or Navy could give a production order for any engine it had to clear the Wright Field acceptance tests (equivalent to the Air Ministry type tests) and General Brett was very keen to obtain the latest mark of engine for this purpose. These tests were constructive in character and he was prepared to allow Rolls-Royce engineers to be present, an exceptional privilege at that time. Maurice Olley kept a diary of these events and has subsequently summarised the outcome of the talks as follows.

General Brett was interested and strongly advocated the development of the Merlin in parallel with the Allison engine for fighter aircraft. Towers, on the other hand, said that the Navy would be interested in putting water-cooled engines into their aircraft on the same day that they installed air-cooled power plants in their submarines.

Unfortunately this request was not considered as the fore-runner of a serious proposal. Sidgreaves thought that the Americans were anxious merely to obtain technical infor-mation and he decided that the United Kingdom could not spare two of the latest engines for this purpose. He replied to Olley that the pressure of Air Ministry orders made it impos-sible to supply two engines. An earlier request transmitted through the American Embassy in London had met with a similar response.

In April Sidgreaves informed McManus that the question of supplying the War Department with sample Merlins in exchange for Allison engines, in which Rolls-Royce was not interested, had become a 'purely political' problem which was being handled by the Air Ministry. On the 9th instructions were received to release two engines and McManus was informed accordingly. Before this the only Merlin in the United States was a specifically finished dummy engine which had been sent over as an exhibit for the World's Fair. Until the new engines arrived, this engine, which was entirely unsuited for the purpose, was in great demand as a sample.

In June the whole situation in the United States became most confused. The question of producing Merlins and the choice of manufacturer had been taken completely out of

Rolls-Royce's hands and Sidgreaves was under the impression that a large order had been given to the Ford Company. The New York *Herald Tribune* reported on 20 June that Lord Beaverbrook had awarded them a contract of 6,000 engines. In Washington it was suspected that this confusion arose as a result of manoeuvring between different manufacturers in the automobile industry, all of whom wanted the publicity which attached to the manufacture of a Rolls-Royce product. A flood of confused cables and letters descended upon Derby from McManus, who, as Sidgreaves later had occasion to point out to Lord Beaverbrook, was 'actuated by an excess of zeal' on Rolls-Royce's behalf. McManus was an intensely jealous guardian of the company's interests and he suspected every manufacturer in the industry of seeking to exploit the goodwill of the name. There was some truth in this but McManus was an unduly ardent collector of ulterior motives. He was consequently inclined to prejudice negotiations by an over-legalistic caution and on several occasions his enthusiasm caused considerable difficulty in both the United States and England.

Full credit must nevertheless be given to this redoubtable trio, McManus, Maurice Olley and their colleague L.G. Ringholz, for the immense energy and drive which they put into the organisation of the Michigan company. Through its early arrival on the scene and because of McManus's appreciation of the fact that small companies were an excellent source of supply – the larger companies having confined work to their own factories in order to justify plant expansion and capital assistance – this company was able to maintain a flow of small tools and parts to the Rolls-Royce and Rotol factories at a time when they could not possibly have been obtained elsewhere.

Mr Kurt Knudsen, then Chairman of General Motors, whom President Roosevelt had brought in to control the Office of Production Management, was primarily responsible for the allocation of the Merlin blueprints and for the approval of any major defence contracts involving the United States Government. On 21 July Maurice Olley visited him at his home to discuss the progress of the Merlin scheme. By this time it had been definitely decided that the Ford Company would not undertake the contract. The general opinion in Washington was that although the Ford Company might have been prepared to build an engine which was similar to the Merlin, the Merlin itself was too intricate a piece of machinery for Ford production methods. One of the main factors responsible for Henry Ford's opposition to the idea was that the contract was with the British as well as the United States Government. He was still of the opinion that any direct orders for Britain should not be handled by his Dearborn works. He did not – in company with many others in June 1940 – entertain very sanguine hopes about the prospects of British survival.

This is what Robert Lacey had to say about Henry Ford's idiosyncratic behaviour in his book *Ford*:

Henry Ford never seems to have been totally clear on the distinction between deploring all war on ethical grounds, and the more politic anxiety to keep America out of whatever mess the rest of the world might get itself into. If America was safe, in his view, there could not be too much wrong with the rest of the planet Earth. So when the Nazi engulfment of Europe provoked a flurry of military preparedness in Washington in the summer of 1940, he proclaimed himself happy to help with the defence of the nation. The Ford Motor Company stood ready, Ford declared on May 28, 1940, to 'swing into a production of a thousand airplanes of standard design a day.'

This was a ludicrous claim. Modern companies, even the producers of quite simple aircraft, do not turn out that number in a year. Henry appears to have been piqued by the news that morning that his former employee, William S. Knudsen, who had risen to the presidency of General Motors and who had, for more than a decade, been directing that corporation in its systematic outclassing of Ford, had just been appointed Commissioner for Industrial Production by President Roosevelt. The Ford Motor Company, said Henry pointedly, would produce its thousand planes a day 'without meddling by Government agencies.' Still, when the War Department sent a pursuit plane to Dearborn so that Ford could examine the possibility of producing it in bulk, Henry consented to Edsel [his son] travelling to Washington to discuss the production details with Knudsen.

The old man appeared agreeable to the proposal which Edsel brought back from Knudsen, that Ford should not so much make planes, to start with, as concentrate on the manufacture of aeroplane engines. With the Battle of Britain reaching its perilous climax, Whitehall had approached Washington to help with the urgent production of 6,000 Rolls-Royce Merlin engines for its Spitfire fighters, and Knudsen thought Ford was the company to do the job.

Edsel and Sorensen were fired with enthusiasm for the project. The Rolls-Royce Merlin represented an ultimate in motor engineering, and quite apart from guaranteed profit, the invitation to produce the engine in bulk provided the finest possible endorsement of Ford manufacturing techniques. Henry Ford allowed Edsel to make the Rolls-Royce project public.

But then Lord Beaverbrook, Minister for War Production in London, hailed the Ford deal as a major step forward in the British war effort, and within hours the phone rang in Knudsen's Washington office. It was Edsel Ford calling from Detroit.

'Bill,' he said, 'we can't make those motors for the British.'

'Why?' asked Knudsen.

'Father won't do it.'

'But you are president of the company.'

'I know, but father won't do it, and you know how he is.'

Knudsen got straight on a plane for Detroit. 'Mr Ford,' he said as he walked into Edsel's office, where Henry and his son were waiting with Charles Sorensen, 'this is terrible about those motors.'

'What motors?' inquired the seventy-seven-year-old carmaker, with one of his innocent, little-boy looks.

'Those motors for the British. Edsel telephoned me and said you wouldn't make them.'

'Nor will we,' snapped Ford.

'There will be a hell of a stink about it if you don't,' said the Industrial Production Commissioner.

'I don't care,' responded Henry Ford, explaining that he was willing to make the motors for Britain if his contract was channelled through the American government, but that he would not sign a contract with the British direct. It was against his principles to provide war materials directly to a foreign belligerent.

This argument might have carried more weight if the Ford Motor Companies of Britain and Germany had not, at that very moment, been producing cars, trucks, and armaments flat out for their respective national war machines. Like General Motors and several other multinational American companies, Ford derived profits in the Second World War from both sides. But logic had never featured prominently in Henry Ford's thinking, and William Knudsen, of all people, understood that.

'Mr Ford,' he remonstrated, sticking to basic principles. 'We have your word that you would make them. I told the President your decision, and he was very happy about it.'

The mention of Roosevelt ended whatever chance Knudsen might have had of salvaging the Rolls-Royce engine deal.

'Withdraw the whole order,' barked Ford, suddenly tense. 'Take it to someone else. Let them build the engine; we won't.'

As Knudsen got up and left the meeting, he was – according to Sorensen – 'purple with rage'. The GM man had started his Washington assignment by offering this job to Ford as a gesture of his good faith and impartiality, and it was a major embarrassment in his first important government venture.

But Knudsen's embarrassment was nothing compared to that of Edsel. Having publicly committed Ford to the contract, he was compelled, three days later, publicly to contradict himself. There was some sort of logic to the about-face which derived from Henry Ford's isolationist principles, but it was too complicated to explain. The only reason that the forty-seven-year-old company president could give for his reneging was that he was doing as his father told him.

As soon as the Ford Company had reached this decision the Packard Company, with whom negotiations had been carried on concurrently by the British Purchasing Commission and the Defence Finance Corporation, was offered the contract and accepted it. The first order was for 9,000 engines, of which 6,000 were for the British Government and 3,000 for the American Government. The first serious offer to the

Packard Company was made by Mr Knudsen on 24 June when he asked the Chairman, Mr Gilman, and the chief engineer, Colonel Vincent, if the Packard Company would consider such an order. The proposal was favourably received and on 26 June a conference on the Merlin 28 was held at the Office of Production Management in Washington. It was decided that the engine was to be duplicated exactly except for pressure-type carburettors, and US standard vacuum pumps, fuel pumps, generators, tachometer drives and other miscellaneous items. On 27 June Mr Knudsen authorised Colonel Vincent to organise a separate engineering division and to proceed at full speed without waiting for contract sanction. The Merlin blueprints, but not the parts which the Ford Company had produced, were taken over the following day. Both capital and current production costs were to be provided by the British and American Governments in the proportion of two-thirds to one-third. The price of the first 1,500 engines was fixed on the basis of cost plus a fixed fee, after which a new fixed price was to be negotiated for the remainder. In the event of failure to agree, the cost plus fixed fee principle was to remain in operation. The two governments acquired an option to purchase a further 10,000 engines in two batches of 5,000 within six months of the completion of the existing contract. It was estimated that the order would cost the British Government about £30,000,000, a staggering sum in 1940 real values, and that the first Packard engines could be expected in the summer of 1941.

With the help of the Rolls-Royce experts, Packard were producing their first engines within a year of the signature of the contract on 3 September 1940. The limitation on the build-up of production was, as was the case at the Glasgow factory, the output of gears. An early hold-up was caused by the sensible decision to stick with all the British threads for reasons of interchangeability. British threads were dated by then, so it was difficult to get the necessary cutting or rolling equipment, especially in wartime and with everyone in the UK overstretched. Nevertheless, by April 1942 production had reached 510 engines per month, and in 1943 averaged 1,024 engines per month. In 1944 it nearly reached 2,000 a month, with a total for that year of 23,619 engines.

Packard supplied Merlin engines to the RAF, which used them in Lancasters, Mosquitoes and Spitfires. Their early engines, Merlin 28s, were similar to the Merlin XX, but had a two-piece block designed in the USA. The Packard Merlin 38s were equivalent to Merlin 22s, and used the Rolls-Royce-designed two-piece cylinder block.

On the Dam Busters raid, the Lancasters used Packard-built Merlin 28s. Packard Merlins for the US Air Force used the designation V1650, with slash numbers to denote the mark. The RAF Mustangs were fitted with V1650-3 or V1650-7 engines. These were two-stage engines, as opposed to the single-stage Merlin 28s.

The major difference between the Rolls-Royce and Packard two-stage Merlins was the supercharger drive. While the former used the Farman drive, the Packard used epicyclic gearing. The single-stage engines were essentially the same. For convenience, Packard used magnetos manufactured in the USA, and carburettors made by Bendix (also in the USA).

Packard made a total of 55,523 Merlins for the RAF and the USAAF. The two-stage Merlin built by Packard also replaced the Allison V1710 in the North American Mustang. The Mustang was first specified and ordered by the British Purchasing Commission in the USA in 1940, when it was seeking to find a fighter to add to the Hurricanes and Spitfires in Britain's offensive and defensive armoury. It was produced in less than four months.

As soon as the agreement between the two governments was finalised it became obvious that the Packard organisation would require technical assistance of the very highest quality – precisely the type of individual who could least be spared from England. Earlier on in 1940 Lord Beaverbrook had insisted that he would not permit any technicians to leave England for any purpose whatever and he had opposed a commendable suggestion that the Bristol and Rolls-Royce development sections should be transferred to Canada (where it was proposed that they should combine) on precisely these grounds. It was nevertheless imperative that Packard be given technical assistance in the interpretation of Rolls-Royce blueprints and production technique and that the closest possible liaison between the two companies should be maintained. On 18 July Olley cabled Derby that 'Gilman regards Packards as started today'. This was followed by a request for eight men and for the latest Griffon drawings since Packards wished to plan the layout of their Merlin line so that it could easily be transferred to the production of Griffons in due course.

On 8 July Sidgreaves asked Lord Beaverbrook for information on certain important points of procedure. He wanted to know whether or not the American engines should be completely interchangeable with the British, what authority Packards would have to depart from British drawings and material specifications and whether they would employ British or American accessories. He also asked whether in the early stages Packards would supply parts to Great Britain as each new factory in Britain had done before it was ready to produce complete engines. All these questions had to be answered before the three Rolls-Royce representatives, Lt.-Colonel T.B. Barrington (chief designer of the Aero Division), J.E. Ellor (development engineer of the Aero Division) and J.M. Reid (production engineer), left for America. Sidgreaves informed Lord Beaverbrook that he was bringing them to see him before they left. 'Although', he added, 'this is a direct contract from the British government to the Packard Company and therefore Rolls-Royce carry no responsibility for the placing or the execution of the contract, it is inevitable that the success of the undertaking will depend on Rolls-Royce and it is certain we shall be blamed for any failure or difficulties which may arise.' All these points were satisfactorily settled by the Minister and the three engineers arrived in America on 2 August to find that the Packard Company, under the immediate direction of the chief engineer, Colonel Vincent, had already shown a good deal of initiative and had made considerable progress. By comparison with the Fordair scheme this was a propitious portent.

SIXTY THOUSAND GAUGES, TOOLS AND FIXTURES

The production of the Merlin engine in the United States was a very considerable undertaking and the relatively short period between the signing of the contract on 3 September 1940 and the production of the first engine in September 1941 was, by any standard, an outstanding achievement. The company planned to produce its first hand-made engine by 20 March 1941, and its first assembly-line engine by 20 July. At the time Hives considered that this was a most optimistic forecast. On 10 October in a report to Lord Beaverbrook he commented on the satisfactory progress being made at the Packard plant. 'The target which Packards have set themselves for delivery is far better than anything we have been able to achieve, but we are not going to say it cannot be done. We want to give them all the help and encouragement we can.' The Packard estimate was not inordinately optimistic, and had the delivery of machine tools been set up to anticipations the target would probably have been achieved. As at Glasgow the main limiting factor in the build-up of production was the output of gears. Quantity production on the British scale was achieved by April 1942 (510 engines) and in 1943 production averaged 1,024 engines a month. In 1944 the stupendous total of 23,169 engines were produced, an average output of 1,930 a month, a figure only some 300 engines less than the average total monthly production of the entire Rolls-Royce group in the same period. The average cost per engine reached a minimum of $11,080 in January 1944 and maintained an overall average of just over $12,000, a figure which did not increase despite the increasing complexity of the latest types of Merlin. In all, 55,000 engines were produced at the Packard plant in Detroit at a total cost of $691,800,000 (including capital assistance provided by both governments). Of this total over 25,000 Merlins were supplied to aircraft manufacturers in Great Britain or other parts of the Empire. These figures pay their own tribute to the productive capacity and flexibility of the industrial system of the democracies in time of war.

As soon as Barrington, Ellor and Reid arrived in the United

101

States they suggested that Packards produce the two-piece cylinder block which had been developed on prototype engines at Derby. This block had been developed to overcome the coolant-leakage difficulties which were anticipated, and which did not fail to materialise, when the decision was taken to use a Kestrel-type head on the Merlin II in order to get a satisfactory engine into production. The Merlin 61 was the first production engine to employ the two-piece block at Derby. In consequence the Packard Merlins, which appeared before the Merlin 61, were the first to incorporate this development. This proposal was acceptable to all concerned at Packards but it was not long before it was realised that the engines produced for the US Government would have to be different – in order to conform to USAAF requirements – from those produced for the RAF. The first major task was to convert British drawings to the third-angle projection type used in the United States. In addition, specifications had to be established for the finish of all parts and placed upon the drawings. This had never been done in England because personnel at Derby had long been accustomed to the required finishes. For mass production these had to be clearly defined.

All this work occupied 75 men continuously for four months. A total of 2,500 drawings were involved and 125,000 prints had to be issued before production could start. The sectioning of sample castings obtained from England revealed that in some cases the drawings did not correspond exactly. These discrepancies had to be cleared up before final production specifications were issued. In addition the designs of some cast aluminium parts had to be revised and the patterns reworked. One of the biggest tasks was the duplication of British Whitworth threads. Not only did Packard find it impossible to obtain all the engineering information which they required to reproduce these threads; they also discovered that all the American firms making taps, dies and thread gauges were already overloaded with work. There was no alternative but to enlist the aid of non-specialist sources in the automobile industry, and this was done.

Practically all the jigs, tools and fixtures required were

special and the majority of them could not be designed until the production studies had been completed and the operations agreed. A total of 60,000 gauges, tools and fixtures were constructed. In the initial stages, when the project did not have a high defence priority rating, production was held up by a shortage of the 3,575 machine tools required to achieve the desired rate of production. Only 10 per cent of the existing tools in the Packard plant were suitable for Merlin production.

In all this work the three Rolls-Royce engineers performed an exacting and prodigious task. Their advice was constantly sought and there is no doubt that had the company sent over men of lesser calibre Packards would not have manufactured their first production engine in 1941. Had the Packard Company acted earlier on Hives's strong recommendation that they should also send some of their best men to England in the early stages, the burden of technical liaison would not have had to be borne entirely by the Rolls-Royce men. Colonel Barrington's death in 1943, shortly after returning from a visit to England, cannot be dissociated from the immense strain which this vast undertaking must have imposed on him.

A large number of purely engineering problems had to be settled, many of them arising out of long-established differences in British and American engineering practices. Their solution was further complicated by the necessity to produce two types of the same mark of engine. In his report on the Packard Merlin, Colonel Vincent made the following comment on his problem:

While we had the wholehearted co-operation of representatives of the Rolls-Royce Company, there was naturally a wide divergence of opinion as to how important engineering items should be handled. For many months the argument centred around what parts should be made special for British engines and during this time our plans were changed from day to day. We started with the understanding that we were to build the same engine for both governments and ended up with the decision to build engines for the British which were installationally interchangeable with British units ... It would be hard to estimate the time that was spent discussing British versus U.S. production, engineering and testing practices but we should not overlook the fact that all concerned received a liberal education that resulted in a definite benefit to both governments.

As Colonel Vincent frankly admitted, the task of producing an aero engine such as the Merlin taxed the resources of his company to the uttermost. 'At the time when our contracts with the British and U.S. Governments were entered into no one in the United States had or could have had any definite idea of the magnitude of the undertaking, which is another way of saying that it would have been impossible to establish accurate production schedules at this time. We know that the suggested schedules were optimistic but we were willing to accept them.' Such clear appreciation of the relationship between programme and uncertainties did not exist in the United Kingdom.

The officials of the Ford Company should be exempted from this criticism since their experience of the Fordair project had provided them with a clear idea of the difficulties involved. It is all the more to the credit of the Packard Company that its management was not daunted by the unknown. From a financial point of view the undertaking was virtually risk-free since the British and American Governments defrayed the entire capital cost as well as production costs; but the engineering risk was considerable.

The production of the Merlin in the Detroit works of the Packard Company marks the final stage in the development and application of quantity production techniques to the manufacture of the Merlin engine. Though not in any way under the direct control of the Rolls-Royce management, the Packard Company was able to draw on the experience accumulated at Derby, Crewe, Glasgow and Fords and to avoid some of the pitfalls which had been discovered in each successive stage of expansion. The Packard management was not saddled with the problem of erecting or equipping a completely new factory, however. The existing floor space was adequate for machining purposes and only an office block and assembly shop had to be specially built. Flow-production methods were developed even further than at Glasgow and Fords to achieve an output of three engines per hour. This set twenty minutes as the maximum time allowed for any single operation. Operations requiring longer than this were broken down and carried out by machines specially designed to complete the process within this limit. The engines were carried on a mechanical conveyor which moved at 40 feet per hour to produce 1,800 engines a month at full production. This example of the mass production of quality might well have impressed even so exacting a critic as Sir Henry Royce.

The Packard scheme was more complete than Crewe from the point of view of dependence on sub-contracting but less complete than Glasgow. Items bought out included fuel pumps, boost control, coolant pump, camshaft, bronze bushes, ball and roller bearings, main and connecting-rod bearings, ignition harnesses, and miscellaneous small items. In the early stages aluminium castings were also bought out. Packards was not, especially in the later stages, absolutely dependent on Derby from the point of view of design and development. The Packard Company carried out independent development work and several interesting and important modifications were made to the design of the American-built Merlin. Some of these, such as the Stromberg carburettor and silver-lead indium bearings, were adopted as soon as the Packard Merlin went into production. Others, such as the planetary supercharger drive mechanism (developed as a result of independent study of the two-stage supercharger problem) and modifications to the coolant pump and the camshaft drive, were made while the engine was in production.

Though all these contributions were most valuable, the outstanding improvements to the engine, which kept it in the forefront until the end of the war, resulted from the intensive development work carried out at Derby. These developments were immediately made available in the United States. In view of the intricate nature of the work, and the long familiarity with an engine which is the most necessary foundation for successful development work, the surprising thing is that the

Packard organisation was able, being so fully occupied with the immense task of production, to carry out any design work or technical development.

The Packard project was impressive in scope and its eventual contribution to the war effort very great, but in the crucial years of 1940 and 1941 the supply of parts and raw materials from the United States was of far greater immediate significance and the build-up of production in the British factories was particularly dependent on the supply of machine tools, ball-bearings and certain other 'bottleneck' items. In 1941 a complete Merlin in a front-line aircraft in North Africa, Burma or the United Kingdom was worth an almost infinite number of Merlins in the process of production at Detroit. In this respect the work of the British Purchasing Commission and of the small company which McManus had incorporated in Michigan under the name Rolls-Royce was of great importance. In the initial stages the Michigan company acted as agent for both Rolls-Royce and Rotols and showed great enterprise in discovering and harnessing sub-contracting capacity. After the passage of the Lend-Lease Act direct purchases with British funds could no longer be made and Rolls-Royce Incorporated thereupon became a direct contractor to the American Government. The volume of orders handled eventually became quite substantial. As far as Merlin production was concerned the most important work of the Michigan company lay in the technical assistance which it gave to companies such as the Wyman-Gordon Company, with whom a large order for crankshaft forgings had been placed soon after the outbreak of the war. Material specifications were often a source of difficulty in obtaining supplies of steels, forgings and other similar products from the United States, and in this respect the work of Dr J.M. Lessels, a metallurgist on the staff of the Massachusetts Institute of Technology, whom Rolls-Royce retained as a consultant, was of great value. The Michigan company provided a headquarters from which all these variegated operations could be carried out and also performed the important task of reporting to England week by week the progress of machine tool and raw material orders. This information made possible much more accurate prediction of the rate of increase in production at the various factories in the group.

Rolls-Royce Managing Director Arthur Sidgreaves was concerned about the dangers of Packard not producing to the required quality, saying:

Although this is a direct contract from the British Government to the Packard Company and therefore Rolls-Royce carry no responsibility for the placing or execution of the contract, it is inevitable that the success of the undertaking will depend on Rolls-Royce and it is certain we shall be blamed for any failure or difficulties which may arise.

Late in 1943, when the success of the Packard Merlin had been proved beyond any doubt, the demands for the engine on both sides of the Atlantic increased so heavily that the US authorities seriously considered expanding production facilities beyond the Packard organisation. The Continental Aircraft Corporation (which had manufactured small-horsepower aero engines before the war) agreed to lay down a Merlin line and preliminary arrangements were made in 1944. The project did not materialise, however, as it became obvious by the middle of 1944 that the additional output would no longer be required.

Major Bulman showed how successful the whole project was when he wrote of the Packard production of Merlins:

The Packard Merlin was virtually interchangeable in detail with the home product except in the supercharger drive which was of Packard design. These American Merlins were of immense help to us in the War from 1940 on [actually 1941], as was the aircraft, named Mustang for the R.A.F. purposes, which became a formidable weapon, augmenting and at times exceeding the performance of the Spitfire against the German fighters. It was so liked by the U.S.A.A.F. that they collared a large proportion of the deliveries, having previously regarded this British intrusion into American aviation with some scorn if not derision!

For inter-Government reasons largely, all correspondence between Rolls-Royce and Packhards [*sic*] passed through my office, and there were never lacking several cables a day to be transmitted with top priority and in code, which became quite a nightmare at times.

The pressure on the three Derby men was immense, and it is significant that Barrington [actually in July 1943] and Jimmy Ellor died soon after the war, far before their time. John Reid retained his native accent, and when I remarked on this following his return home, he grinned and said 'Aye but they are all talking broad Lancashire now out there.' It was the devotion of men like these on which British aero engines was sustained, though for most of them their very names have long been forgotten.

CHAPTER FIVE

'THE MERLIN HAS ONLY JUST STARTED ITS USEFUL LIFE'

THE BATTLE OF BRITAIN
'YOU CAN'T BLOW UP A ROLLS-ROYCE ENGINE'
'HE CARES FOR NOTHING BUT THE DEFEAT OF GERMANY'
THE SUPERCHARGER
RADAR, PROPELLERS AND FUEL

THE BATTLE OF BRITAIN

The first triumph of the Merlin engine during the war was to power the two fighter aircraft that overcame the Luftwaffe in what became known as the Battle of Britain.

Pausing after the victory over France the Luftwaffe contented itself in July 1940 with attacking convoys in the English Channel and British ports, but it knew that to complete a successful invasion of the British Isles it would be necessary to gain command of the skies. The RAF and their bases of operation would have to be destroyed. During the early part of August the Luftwaffe began to attack British airfields. The puffed-up, though nevertheless threatening Goering made light of the protests of other Luftwaffe commanders over the difficulties and told them:

The Führer has ordered me to crush Britain with my Luftwaffe. By means of hard blows I plan to have this enemy, who has already suffered a crushing moral defeat, down on his knees in the nearest future, so that an occupation of the island by our troops can proceed without any risk!

Opposing the 654 aircraft in Fighter Command were 1,971 German aircraft, including 594 of their best fighter, the Messerschmitt Bf 109E. Emil ('Willi') Messerschmitt, the son of a Frankfurt wine merchant, had been born three years after Mitchell and, like him, became a passionate air enthusiast during his childhood. His early design work was on gliders, and he designed one or two not very successful aircraft before turning his attention to a fighter in the early 1930s. As we have seen, in one of those strange quirks of history, the prototype of his Bf 109, precursor to the famous Bf 109E, was powered by an imported Rolls-Royce Kestrel engine (as was the Junkers JU 87, the Stuka). This engine was soon replaced by the German Jumo 210D, and when the Bf 109E was developed in 1938, it was fitted with the Daimler-Benz 601A engine, which generated 400 extra horsepower for its extra 400 lb of weight.

On 15 August, the Luftwaffe launched its main attack on what was code-named Adlertag (Eagle Day). It was not a great success. The Germans lost 75 aircraft, but the British lost 30 in the air and another 24 on the ground. In his book *A Short History of Air Power*, James Stokesbury tells the story of the next few days:

This fighting went on for three more days, with losses too heavy to bear on both sides. Fighter Command won its only Victoria Cross on August 16, when Lieutenant J.B. Nicholson stayed in his burning Hurricane to shoot down a Messerschmitt. The highly touted and much feared JU 87 Stuka proved such an easy mark for the British fighters that it was withdrawn from the battle, and by August 18 the Germans had to pause for breath.

No one could tell how he was doing. By accepting pilots' claims, the Germans thought they should already have destroyed the British, yet obviously they were still there. Every time the Luftwaffe flew a raid, there were a handful of Hurricanes or a pair of Spitfires coming down out of the sun to meet them.

The last week of August and the first week of September proved the crucial period for the RAF. In those two weeks the Germans finally got their priorities correct and went after the whole structure of Fighter Command – the radar stations, the airfields, the control mechanisms. They also increased the number of free-fighter sweeps, and, by unremitting pressure, they began to win. Some of the radar went out, a couple of the most forward airfields were untenable and, most important of all, pilot attrition was wearing down the fighter strength. Dowding was scrounging pilots from Coastal Command, the Fleet Air Arm, any place he could get them. The British were feeding in Polish and Czech refugee pilots who could barely understand English commands over the radio, and by September 7 they were palpably losing. In two weeks they lost 264 fighters, and though many of their pilots parachuted or crash-landed on their own territory and lived to fight again, many did not. They went to sea, they were burned, shot or invalided, and their places had to be taken by younger, less experienced, and more vulnerable fliers. The attrition rate was just as bad for the Germans, worse, in fact, as they were fighting over enemy territory, but there were more Germans to get through. [This may not be completely accurate. The way the Luftwaffe drove its pilots – demanding more missions and sending them up while still recovering from wounds – suggests that it was as short of pilots as the RAF.] In a war of attrition the side that can stay longer wins. The Germans were now winning. Dowding believed that three more weeks would destroy his command, thereby opening England to invasion. The Germans were collecting barges along the coast.

On September 7 Goering threw victory away. Believing the exaggerated claims of his pilots, steadfastly misunderstanding the nature of his enemy, and indeed of air war, he decided the British were already finished. He thought Fighter Command was a broken reed; the battle was won. On September 7 he ordered the *coup de grace* for England. The army and the navy were all but ready to go; moon and tide would be right from September 8 through September 10. The British had put out an invasion warning, and on the afternoon of September 7, more than a thousand aircraft took off from bases across the Channel, formed up in massive units, and droned out towards England.

Park [later Air Chief Marshal Sir Keith Park, he commanded the vital No. 11 Fighter Group during the Battle of Britain] and his 11 Group watched them come with grim determination. They knew it was all over; the thin blue line was fraying out into invisibility.

111

Waiting for their last best shot, they watched for the Germans to break up and head for the airfields and factories; while they did, the huge armada droned stolidly on, disdaining targets in the flat green countryside below. Incredulously, almost too late to do anything to stop it, the British realized the Germans were heading straight for London itself.

While Park called in every fighter he could find, the Germans bombed the London docks and the East End. Immense fires piled up into the sky, to last all night and be seen a hundred miles away. Hermann Goering, whose pilots sometimes unkindly called him 'Nero' in reference to his pretensions and pomposity [and possibly his addiction to drugs], stood on the cliffs at Calais and warmed himself with the glow of London burning. His cup ran over. He did not know he had just lost his war.

Goering may have made a fatal mistake in attacking London instead of continuing to destroy the airfields, but critical battles are won and lost for a variety of reasons. The Spitfires and Hurricanes, flown by their indomitable pilots, and positioned and preserved by intelligent and resourceful leaders, had withstood the might of the Luftwaffe, which at that time outnumbered them three to one. Both aeroplanes were powered by Rolls-Royce Merlin engines. What was the verdict of those that flew them?

An expert judgement came from Jeffrey Quill, of whom Sir George Edwards OM said: 'Jeffrey Quill was one of the most articulate test pilots I ever encountered ... and to him goes much of the credit for turning Mitchell's brilliant concept into a great fighting machine.' In his book *Spitfire, A Test Pilot's Story*, published by John Murray in 1983, Quill wrote:

At the end of it all I felt a very friendly disposition towards the new Merlin engine. It started for me a process of confidence in that remarkable piece of machinery which was to grow ever stronger as my hours in the air with it increased and as progressively I demanded more and more from it in the way of continuous running at full power in the course of rigorous performance testing. I learned to be meticulous in the matter of correct engine handling at all times and although I never hesitated to run it to the absolute limit of its capabilities I was careful never to exceed those limits except when unavoidable. In return the Merlin hardly ever let me down and such total power failures as I experienced – and over the years inevitably there were many – were due as often as not to extraneous causes rather than to anything fundamental to the engine. The Merlin really was the pilot's friend.

Duncan Smith, later Group Captain W.G. Duncan Smith DSO DFC, said of the Spitfire and Merlin:

611 Squadron were equipped with MK 1 Spitfires, some with pump-handle operated landing gear and others with recently modified gear which was hydraulic operated. The engines were Rolls-Royce Merlin IIs rated at 1,050 hp [Smith is understating the performance. By the time of the Battle of Britain, 100 octane fuel was being used and the performance was 1,250–1,300 hp]. The aircraft was a joy to fly and its armament of eight Brownings and splendid handling qualities gave me a confidence in the Spitfire that stayed with me through operational experiences spanning eleven different Marks. One has, of course, to include the various types of Rolls-Royce engines that powered Spitfires over a period of many years. Reliable to an extent that was fantastically excellent, never did I ever think I would be let down by engine or airframe. One could stretch both to the very edge of disaster and yet feel fully confident in the operating ability of both.

Wing Commander Stanford Tuck, one of the heroes of the Battle of Britain, described the Spitfire as 'thirty feet of wicked beauty ... with practically no relation to any of the aircraft I'd flown previously'. Group Captain Douglas Bader, who lost both his legs in a flying stunt in the early 1930s and was allowed back into the RAF when war broke out, described the Spitfire as behaving like 'a highly strung thoroughbred'.

'YOU CAN'T BLOW UP A ROLLS-ROYCE ENGINE'

The development of the Spitfire from the Mark I of 1938 through to the Seafire FMK 47 which was twice as heavy, whose maximum horsepower was more than double, whose maximum speed was 90 mph greater, whose maximum rate of climb was almost double and whose range was almost three times as far, would not have been possible without the parallel development of its engines, the Merlin and the Griffon. Indeed, as Jeffrey Quill pointed out, 'to a large extent it was engine development and power growth that led the way'. Not only was the power of the Merlin increased from 1,000 bhp in 1936 to over 2,000 bhp in 1944, the band of heights at which the power was available nearly doubled from 16,000 to 30,000 feet, which was of considerable tactical significance.

The Spitfire in the form of the Seafire became a Naval carrier-borne fighter and also a long-range, unarmed, high-speed, high-altitude photographic reconnaissance aeroplane. But the Spitfire was at its best as a fighter, and this meant that its pilots were looking for more speed, higher rates of climb, better manoeuvrability, more firepower, greater range and endurance. It was nearly always more power, or the same power at a greater height, from the Rolls-Royce engines that would lead to a new mark of Spitfire which would then be able to incorporate heavier armaments, fly further, faster and higher and therefore enjoy a greater role capability.

There were many different models, from Spitfire I in the later 1930s through to the Spitfire XIX of 1945 and the 21, 22 and 24 of the post-war years. However, the leaps forward in performance all came about through the improved performance of the Merlin and, latterly, the Griffon. Indeed, in a memo to Sir Wilfrid Freeman on 8 November 1942, Hives complained about both the lack of improvement in the Spitfire itself and the constant search for a dramatically new aircraft that would transform the war:

We started the war with two very good fighters – the Spitfire and the Hurricane – and the progress which has been made up-to-date is that we are now left with only one – the Spitfire. It is fortunate that the Spitfire has the fundamentals of an ideal fighting machine. We do not think a better fighter can be produced and in quantities before 1944. We should like to see this recognised and accepted, and, having been accepted, there should be a steady development on the aircraft side comparable with what we are planning for the engine.

There are one or two obvious faults on the Spitfire which ought to be and could be improved if there was the will and the desire to do it, and not this craving to produce something different. The manufacturing finish of the Spitfire is bad. This is shown up by the variation from machine to machine in performance, and the controls. We do not think it is sufficient to improve the paintwork, although this is the last thing we should want to stop, but given a continuity of production we should expect the aircraft to be manufactured to a higher quality.

The controls on the Spitfire compare very unfavourably with either the Fw 190 or the Mustang. As we increase the performance of the machine, these faults show up to a greater degree, but the controls can be and should be improved.

Earlier, at the beginning of 1940, the RAF knew that more power was needed at altitude. Rolls-Royce felt that they could achieve this, but the drawback was a loss of power at sea-level. The solution was the Merlin XX with Hooker's supercharger, which gave power at altitude and also maintained it at lower altitudes through a second gear on the supercharger. Early in 1940, both Hawker and Supermarine were looking at ways of installing the Merlin XX in the Hurricane and the Spitfire. Hawker were able to accommodate the extra length of the Merlin XX, and Hurricanes with this new engine saw action at the end of the Battle of Britain. Supermarine found it more difficult, and decided that the Merlin XX should be fitted into the new Spitfire III. Unfortunately, the development and production of this airframe had to take second place to the priority of producing Spitfire Is and IIs.

By the winter of 1940, it was becoming clear that the Messerschmitt Bf 109 was beginning to outpace the Spitfire Is and IIs. The improved Spitfire III with the Merlin XX would not be available for the anticipated spring offensive of the Luftwaffe. Just before Christmas 1940, Hives met Henry Tizard and Sholto Douglas at the Aircraft and Armament Evaluation Establishment at Boscombe Down, and suggested that Rolls-Royce should fit into the Spitfire a Merlin RM5S, a Merlin III fitted with Stanley Hooker's new central-entry super-charger but without the two-speed drive. The significance of leaving out the two-speed drive was that the original length of the engine was retained, but the engine still gave enhanced power at fighting altitudes. Furthermore, Hives undertook to carry out the first 50 conversions at Hucknall. This stop-gap Spitfire became the famous Mark V with the Merlin 45, ulti-mately the Spitfire with the highest production run.

As development work continued around the clock to achieve greater speed and performance, it was heartening for Hives to receive letters of appreciation from the front line. Air Marshal Dawson, in charge of RAF engineering in North Africa, wrote from Headquarters, Royal Air Force, Cairo on 7 June 1941:

I thought this message would interest you, and might be the sort of thing you would like to display in the works.

I was talking to-day to the Squadron Commander of an Australian Fighter Squadron which has been using Hurricanes in the Western Desert. I asked him about my old friend the 12 lb boost. He said: 'You can't blow up a Rolls-Royce engine. I would fly behind a Merlin anywhere.'

This sort of feeling after the struggle they have had in the Western Desert is something to be remembered. I thought you would like to have the message.

And again on 23 February 1942:

You will like to know that the Merlins have given surprisingly little trouble considering the appalling conditions under which they run. The requirement for an engine out here is that it must stand up to sand in the intake; however efficient the air cleaners may be, sand gets through and it is quite impossible to clean them adequately in the desert.

The Merlin XXs have been particularly successful, so far – touch wood – no trouble at all. The engines are good, the aeroplanes are good, the worst feature is the installation. There seems to be no clear appreciation of overseas conditions and what is necessary in order to ensure success. Tomahawks were lucky because they had a top air intake and a downdraught carburettor placed so that little sand seemed to get in; this does not always apply: on the Bostons, although there is a downdraught carburettor and a top intake, sand goes straight in picked up by the airscrews and also spraying off the nosewheel.

The best position for the intake appears to be as near the airscrew disc as possible and close to the hub, but it is quite clear to us here that these things have not been properly considered in design and production in sufficient time. Bostons and Baltimores all have to have the intakes moved here and filters fitted. The very 'fine' lubrication condition in the R.2600 won't stand up to desert sand: we have to fit up special scraper rings in order to prevent the engines becoming unserviceable due to heavy oil consumption in a very short time.

Incidentally, in order to be economical and because supplies cannot be maintained, we rebuild Merlins with reground piston rings and are chromium plating the cylinder barrels and regrinding and lapping.

This sand is a great problem here. The Germans use a filter intake with a special bypass shutter which they can open when they are in the air. It is a good scheme; we should have done it earlier on.

The pressure for improved performance was always present. In August 1941, Air Marshal Sholto Douglas, by now Commander in Chief, Fighter Command, submitted a memorandum to the Chief of the Air Staff marked 'Most Secret'. It expressed grave concern about whether Fighter Command, equipped with Spitfire Mark Vs, would be able to maintain parity with the Luftwaffe by the spring of 1942. It noted that the Spitfire was already inferior to the Messerschmitt 109F in speed and climb at heights above 31,000 feet. While the Air Ministry chiefs were considering this memorandum during the autumn of 1941, increasing numbers of Focke-Wulf 190s were appearing. This aircraft was proving itself more manoeuvrable and heavily armed than even the versatile Bf 109F. By this time, there were plenty of people, including rival manufacturers, claiming that the Spitfire was past it.

Hives warned that the only way to *guarantee* having a better aeroplane a year in the future was to improve on what you had *now*. Both Hives and Lovesey were aware of the possible improvements that could be made to engines, but they also knew that they would take time to develop and manufacture. The Luftwaffe had to be tackled today, tomorrow and the day after that, not some time next year. He was not sure where he had read it, but Hives was fond of quoting the line: 'The better is the enemy of the good.' Lovesey talked of 'infiltrating' modifications into production. Both he and Hives were only too aware of the enhanced performance of the Bf 109F – Bill Lappin, through his work in liaising with the RAF, would have kept them fully informed.

The Merlin 60 had been conceived as a high-altitude engine for the Wellington bomber, effectively a replacement for the Hercules. The engine ran for the first time in the spring of 1941, and Hives and Lovesey felt it would be an ideal engine, with suitable changes to the supercharger gearing to optimise power at the required altitudes for a fighter, to install in the Spitfire. Lovesey instructed Hucknall to install this modified Merlin 60, called the Merlin 61, into a Spitfire V airframe. This became the Spitfire IX. Its performance was a revelation, and another aircraft was converted and sent to Boscombe Down for evaluation by the RAF.

'Knocking' of the Merlin had started as early as 1937, as we can see from a report written by Hives on 16 December that year, in which he said:

We consider that it is in the interests of the Air Ministry as well as Rolls-Royce Limited, that the statement which has been made that the Merlin engine is out-of-date should be contradicted.

The Merlin engine has only just started its useful life, and unless the whole of the experience of all makes of aero engines is to be disregarded, the Merlin should have a useful life of five or six years. [With development, its useful life proved to be much longer than five or six years!] Look in any direction you like and it can be proved that more improvements on aero engines have come from development rather than design ...

118

... We do not think it is realised sufficiently that the Merlin engine is the most powerful engine in production in the world today. [This comment followed a report from Major Bulman at the Air Ministry, after his visit to Germany, stating that air-cooled engines were going to be more powerful than the Merlin.]

Hives continued:

If we are going to be judged on what it is assumed the output from the German engines might be some day, then it must naturally follow that these should be compared with our projected Merlin powers.

And on 16 October, just after what later became known as the Battle of Britain, a battle in which the Merlin had surely proved itself as much as the Hurricane and Spitfire, Sidgreaves felt obliged to send a report to Lord Beaverbrook complaining about the loose talk in the press praising 'wonderful new fighter aircraft which the RAF possess':

MINISTER OF AIRCRAFT PRODUCTION There is only one object in writing this report, and that is with the idea of helping the Minister of Aircraft Production in his most difficult job and tremendous responsibility.

The reason we claim that we may help you is that there is no other aero engine firm in this country which has had the same experience as Rolls-Royce. We are the only firm designing and producing aero engines in this country to-day who were producing their engines during the last war, and we contributed considerably to the success of the R.F.C. and the R.N.A.S. The Bristol Engine Company did not exist at that time, although Mr. Fedden was employed by Brazil Strakers, who were subcontractors of Rolls-Royce. Napiers attempted to produce aero engines, but their contribution was practically nil. Armstrong Siddeley made a large number of engines, but they were not designed by them.

During our 25 years' experience of producing aero engines we have watched the rise and fall of Air Ministers, and the coming and going of senior R.A.F. Officers, and our long experience has enabled us to formulate a correction factor for the Civil Service.

Consistently every few years we have been faced with some wonderful new engine, which was the last word in performance and efficiency, and told that it was only a matter of time before Rolls-Royce would be out of business. There have been times when we have been so impressed with the information that we have believed it ourselves, but fortunately we have never believed it to the extent of dropping the substance and chasing the shadow. It has been embarrassing at times because some of the senior technical officials at the Air Ministry have backed these projects to an extent far beyond what was justified and proved by subsequent results.

Our anxiety at the present time, which is the most dangerous and critical in our history, is whether experience is being overlooked. We read in the press about the wonderful new fighter aircraft which the R.A.F. possess. It gives one the impression that the Spitfires and Hurricanes are already out of date. It may be necessary to publish these things, but there is always the danger that if a thing is said often enough, even people who know better accept it as a fact. The fighter pilots, who know very little of what is going on technically, will get the impression that they are being sent into the air with an out-of-date machine.

We know the position as regards fighter aircraft, and it is positively certain that the only machines we shall have to fight the Germans with in 1941 are the Hurricanes and Spitfires. The fact that we may have a few Westland fighters and Beaufighters and other odds and ends will provide just a mere irritation; the basis of the fighters for 1941 is positively Hurricanes and Spitfires. If this is accepted, which it must be, then every effort should be made to ensure that those Hurricanes and Spitfires are as good as we know how to make them. We are not at all satisfied that this is being done, in fact we are certain that it is not.

'HE CARES FOR NOTHING BUT THE DEFEAT OF GERMANY'

Sir Wilfrid Freeman appreciated the significance of Hives's (and therefore Rolls-Royce's) single-mindedness in concentrating on producing Merlins. They wrote to each other frequently and frankly, and met occasionally, even though according to

Air Ministry rules this was not allowed. Freeman deeply admired Hives, and credited him with giving the Spitfire a qualitative superiority over enemy fighters. He was to say of Hives in 1944:

That man Hives is the best man I have come across for many a year. God knows where the RAF would have been without him. He cares for nothing except the defeat of Germany and he does all his work to that end, living a life of unending labour.

Following the introduction of the Focke-Wulf 190, a crash programme was put in hand to convert the Spitfire Vc to the Merlin 61 engine which, as we have seen, had been developed by Rolls-Royce following their work on engines for the high-altitude Wellington. The conversion meant a substantial modification to the cooling system, which involved the fitting of an additional external radiator under the starboard wing, as well as a new and larger oil cooler unit and the fitting of an intercooler radiator in the port duct. In turn, this necessitated considerable modification to the pipe runs. New engine cowlings and a four-bladed Rotol propeller were also required. Eventually the Spitfire IX emerged, a highly successful variant, of which 5,665 were built. When it was introduced it gave a great boost to morale. As Jeffrey Quill said:

The great thing about the appearance of the MKIX at that juncture was that it was extremely difficult for the German pilots to distinguish a MKIX from a MKV in the air. Therefore every Spitfire in the sky soon became potentially a MKIX to the German pilots. This had a marked effect upon their confidence and thus upon the level of their aggressive tactics.

However, the British feeling of superiority was soon brought down to earth with a bump when, on 23 June 1942, a German pilot, disorientated after a battle with Spitfires over the Channel, landed his Fw 190 at Pembrey in South Wales. The aircraft, undamaged, was quickly despatched to RAE at Farnborough, where tests were carried out in a trial against the

Spitfire Mark IX. These trials showed that the edge the Spitfire held over the Fw 190 was much narrower than had been thought. Indeed, between 15,000 and 23,000 feet, the rate of climb of the Fw 190 was faster. Its lateral manoeuvrability was also noted, and it was acknowledged that the Focke-Wulf was superior to the Spitfire generally at low altitudes.

Shortly afterwards, on 14 July, the new Minister of Aircraft Production, Colonel Llewellyn, made a statement in the House of Commons implying that the British fighter aircraft were superior to their German counterparts in all respects. This statement led to the Chief of the Air Staff complaining to Sir Archibald Sinclair, the Secretary of State for Air, that the Minister's statement was inaccurate, and that in the very important height band of 15,000–25,000 feet the Spitfire Mark IX's rate of climb was inferior to that of the Fw 190. Moreover, most of the Spitfires in Fighter Command were Mark Vs, which were considerably inferior to the Fw 190. These exchanges soon brought demands on Rolls-Royce for even greater performance from the Merlin 61. In the short term, the company was able to produce an increase in allowable manifold pressure for combat from plus 12 lb to plus 15 lb, with the hope that 18 lb would soon be achieved. In the longer term, it resulted in the re-scheduling of both the low and high blower gear ratios, which brought better performance at the low and medium altitudes at the expense of the higher altitudes. Thus the 15,000–25,000 feet gap was filled. This new engine – the Merlin 66 – was in production by early 1943, and was fitted into the Spitfire Mark IX. Alan ('Al') Deere, one of the most successful fighter pilots of the war, wrote later:

The Spitfire MKIX attained its best performance at 21,000 feet, or at roughly the same altitude as did the Focke-Wulf 190. At this height it was approximately 30 mph faster, was better in the climb and vastly more manoeuvrable. As an all-round fighter, the Spitfire IX was supreme, undoubtedly the best Mark of Spitfire produced, despite later and more powerful versions.

Group Captain (later Air Vice-Marshal) Johnnie Johnson agreed with Deere.

We flew hard during those summer months of 1943 and scored some decisive successes against the Luftwaffe. Our Spitfire IXs were superior to both the Focke-Wulf 190 and the latest Messerschmitt product, the 109G.

The Merlin was initially designed to power air defence fighters, but it was also used in the Fairey Battle day bomber and in the Armstrong Whitworth Whitley IV and V heavy bombers, as well as in the Vickers-Armstrong Wellington II and the four-engine Handley Page Halifax. Some 1,650 Whitleys, 440 Wellingtons and 3,000 Halifaxes were produced. The Halifax was the third of the trio that made up the bulk of Bomber Command's aircraft, alongside the Stirling and the Lancaster. Like the Lancaster, it was originally designed as a two-engine aircraft but was subsequently modified to take four engines. The Lancaster, originally called the Avro Manchester III, was renamed after the failure of the Avro Manchester with its Vulture engines.

In his book *The Avro Lancaster* Francis Mason goes into great detail about the development of the Manchester and its replacement by the Lancaster. His conclusion is that pressure for a new bomber forced the pace too hard, both for the airframe and for the engine manufacturer. The origin of the Rolls-Royce Vulture was the search for a high-powered engine with more potential than the Buzzard. In the mid-1930s, Rowledge developed an engine which was essentially one Kestrel above another, one upside down, and both using the same crankshaft. The first prototype ran in September 1937, the second in January 1938 and the third in May 1938. Following lessons learnt, a prototype Vulture II, with a two-speed supercharger, ran in September 1938.

Testing continued into 1939 and, in the light of experience with the Merlin and other engines, major modifications were made to Vulture I so that Vulture II appeared not only with an improved supercharger, but also with a down-draught carburettor, a modified ignition set-up, and a number of other improvements. It passed its type test quite quickly and went into production. However, it soon ran into problems.

The first was that one half of the split cooling system could airlock and the coolant flow into two cylinder blocks could cease, with subsequent piston seizure. Once the mechanism was established, the cure, a balancing bleed between the two coolant pumps, was not difficult. The second problem was more serious and more difficult: bearing and con-rod failures. The con-rod arrangement was that there was one master con-rod with a full-size big-end on the crank-pin. The other three pistons had con-rods which had a gudgeon pin at each end, one in the piston and the other in a similar bearing in the master rod big-end. Originally it was thought that the problem lay in the master rod big-end, but deeper investigation indicated that the two halves of the crankcase had been moving relative to each other. In the X formation, each half crankcase carries half of each main bearing; this meant that the movement affected the main bearings, and through them the big-ends. The problem was cured by fitting one-inch-diameter steel dowels in each crankcase end panel to ensure positive location of the two halves with each other.

The Vulture V with these various modifications was a very satisfactory engine, even at ratings higher than the Vulture II. There were some continuing difficulties, but these were allied to the installation rather than the engine. The Manchester suffered from design faults on the airframe, and it was soon realised that the wingspan would need to be increased and extra tail-fins added. The Vulture engine was prone to two sorts of failure. First, it tended to throw con-rods, either through lack of oil or because of the mechanical loads on the big-ends at maximum rpm. Second, it overheated and the Glycol coolant caught fire. This was not the fault of the Vulture engine itself, but rather of the installation, designed by Avro. The cowling was too close to the engine, and did not allow sufficient ventilation.

However, the damage had been done. The Manchester had already built up a bad reputation from which it would be

17. Hives's son, pilot Officer Ted Hives, tragically
killed in action.

18. Merlins being repaired at the Rolls-Royce
works in Nottingham.

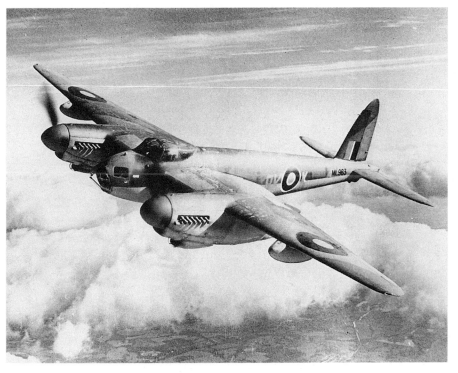

19. A Merlin-powered de Havilland Mosquito
light bomber.

20. Repairing Merlin-powered Hawker Hurricanes at Rolls-Royce's Hucknall works in 1941.

ROLLS-ROYCE LIMITED

NOTICE

As a result of the instruction given by the Minister of Aircraft Production, supplemented by the statements of the other Supply Ministers, and confirmed by Parliament, increased production of engine supplies is vitally necessary.

The co-operation of all employees to this end is looked for with confidence and, as from Saturday, 25th May, the following hours will be obligatory throughout the Factory and Offices :—

DAY SHIFT 7.55 a.m. to 7.45 p.m.
NIGHT SHIFT 8.0 p.m. to 7.45 a.m.

One hour will be allowed for dinner and half an hour for tea.

All production departments, including services and tool room, are to be staffed fully during nights and such office and clerical staffs as are found to be necessary will be notified by their departmental chiefs.

E. W. HIVES
Deputy Controller

24/5/40

21. The reality of war – virtually a twelve-hour working day, seven days a week.

22. A Merlin ready for despatch at Rolls-Royce's
Crewe works.

23. Sir Stafford Cripps, Minister of Aircraft Production, in conversation with Hives. Harold Wilson, later Labour Prime Minister, is standing between them.

24. A Spitfire MK V powered by a Merlin 45. This became
the Spitfire with the longest production run.

difficult to recover, and Avro were now looking into the four Merlin engine idea. However, the Napier Sabre had reached the stage at which it could be a relatively easy replacement for the Vulture in this and other possible applications. It was therefore logical to drop the Vulture so that Rolls-Royce could concentrate on the Griffon, for which there was no ready replacement.

A.A. Rubbra, closely involved in the development of the Vulture, wrote later about the engine's problems:

A serious trouble arose on the first production engines due to main bearing failures which were eventually traced to the top and bottom halves of the main bearings being built out-of-line. The bolting together of the two crankcase halves was achieved by what were known as cross-bolts which were positioned normal to the cylinder facing in order to deal directly with the explosion loadings arising from the cylinder blocks. These bolts being slightly staggered fore and aft to clear one another where they cross on the split line. Although a step was provided in the joint face between the halves of the crankcase to align them, this was not sufficient to prevent transverse slight relative movement applied at 45 degrees through the joint face and dependent on the order of tightening of bolts. The condition was slightly improved by imposing a rigid tightening order but was finally cured by the provision of cylindrical dowels, in the form of 'cheeses', which were large enough in diameter to allow the cross-bolts to pass through them; this also provided for location of the dowel endwise. With this modification no further main bearing trouble was experienced.

One item of interest was the burning out of certain cylinder blocks as a result of the breakdown in the coolant circulation. The Vulture had two coolant pumps in parallel, with the result that one pump could get a complete breakdown in flow due to cavitation at its inlet, whilst the other pump maintained full flow. This effect was investigated by making the two pumps in a transparent material and the solution was to balance the inlet pressures to the two pumps by introducing a balance pipe.

Unfortunately in service as the engine of the Manchester bomber a number of connecting rod bolt failures occurred. As a result several aircraft were lost, causing a crisis in Bomber Command. It was this problem and the decision to use 4 Merlins instead of 2 Vultures, leading to the highly successful Lancaster, that caused the Vulture to be stopped, as the great power potential of the Merlin was then being appreciated.

Ronnie Harker, one of Rolls-Royce's liaison test pilots, remembered that although the Vulture problems were overcome, it was not before a number of Manchesters were lost, and he witnessed the loss of the test aircraft. It should be noted that a number of the crashes were not caused by the failure of the Vulture engine.

For example, on its first flight from Ringway to Boscombe Down, the crew switched on the reserve instead of the main fuel tank and the fuel ran out. At Boscombe Down itself, the piston failed because the wrong spark plugs had been fitted. These were bought by a Government agency and fitting them was not the responsibility of Rolls-Royce engineers. Another crash at Woodford was the result of bearing failures. Furthermore, the weight of the Manchester kept increasing, and Rolls-Royce increased the power of the Vulture accordingly, but in the end the aircraft was too heavy to fly on one engine. This meant that any trouble with one engine would mean a crash landing.

Harker wrote later in his book *The Engines Were Rolls-Royce*:

I happened to have flown over to Ternhill Aerodrome where I was giving a talk to the pilots of the fighter conversion unit. I was standing on the aerodrome talking to Squadron Leader Gerry Edge who, incidentally, was to become godfather to my second daughter! He was a good friend of mine and I had joined his 605 Squadron at the end of the Battle of Britain, where it was operating from Croydon. It had been the first squadron equipped with the Hurricane Mark II. Group Captain Teddy Donaldson, who was the station commander, was also with us.

We saw a Manchester approaching the aerodrome with one engine on fire. The pilot, Reg Curlew, one of our test pilots, and very experienced on large multi-engined aircraft, seemed to be well in control; he was making a downwind approach with enough height, so it seemed, to be able at least to turn and land across-wind. He must have thought he could get round into wind, so he continued the circuit before turning into wind for the final approach. Alas, he undershot and landed just short of the aerodrome in a field which had some large trees in it. He hit one of these and a wing was pulled off, rupturing the fuel tank; there was an explosion and the whole aeroplane went up in flames. We rushed to the spot in the group captain's car only to find a mass of flames; the two flight observers had managed to crawl out of the rear door and were not badly burned but there was no sign of Reg Curlew. Gerry Edge and Teddy Donaldson, amidst the exploding ammunition, did get into the aircraft by the rear door for a few moments. Gerry Edge said he saw the pilot still in his seat but crushed against the control column and obviously either dead or unconscious. One of the tyres then burst, the aircraft settled down and another tank burst so Gerry made a hurried retreat, getting out just in the nick of time before the whole thing became one mass of flames.

Major Bulman, a key figure at the Air Ministry, recalled that after this crash

Air Marshal Tedder and Sir Wilfrid Freeman went to Avros just after this prototype had spun in, and Dobbie Dobson the irrepressible [Sir Roy Dobson, Managing Director of A.V. Roe Ltd.], with a model Manchester in his hand, said none of them were happy with results to date and that Rolls-Royce seemed lukewarm about the Vultures. Whereupon he slipped off the model's wing and replaced it with another mounting four Merlins. Hence the Lancaster which was destined to become the best British bomber of the war. No doubt Hives had warning of this vital change in talks with Dobbie, and may even have inspired the thought in Dobbie's mercurial brain.

Dave Piggott has no doubt that Hives would have suggested that the Vulture be replaced by the Merlin. He pointed out that Rolls-Royce were looking for a replacement for the Vulture as early as 1937. The Vulture was Kestrel technology, and the company was developing a more modern 2,000 hp, 24-cylinder X engine known as PV24. However, as war became more and more likely, Hives stopped development work on it so that resources could be concentrated on the Merlin and Griffon. In spite of all Hives's efforts to persuade Dobson to replace two Vultures with four Merlins, he needed the help of Sir Wilfrid Freeman to clinch the argument. This was made clear in a letter written by Hives to Sir John Slessor in the 1950s, after Slessor had given an address on Battle of Britain Day in which he praised the contribution of Freeman. After acknowledging Freeman's help with the development of the Merlin, and in persuading Ford to produce them in Manchester, he added:

One of the particular projects where he actually, in spite of all our efforts, had to give a final push was to make the Lancaster with 4 Merlins instead of with 2 Vultures.

The Lancaster, with its four Merlin XX or 22 engines, or Packard Merlin 28, 38, 24 and 224 engines, gradually became the dominant force in Bomber Command, and turned out to be their success of the war. Serving from January 1942, it dropped just over 60 per cent of Bomber Command's entire bomb tonnage in the war. Some 4,000 of the 7,300 Lancasters built were lost, mainly in action, while nine of the 32 Victoria Crosses awarded to air crews went to Lancaster crews. Air Chief Marshal 'Bomber' Harris called the Lancaster 'a shining sword in the hands of Bomber Command'.

As well as powering Spitfires, Hurricanes and Lancasters, the Merlin was also fitted into other wartime aircraft. The Mosquito, designed by Bishop and Clarkson of de Havilland, was a wooden-airframed aircraft designed as a bomber with the performance of a fighter. It could fly at high altitudes and was therefore virtually invulnerable to anti-aircraft fire. It was also difficult to intercept, and these two factors made it very popular with the RAF. Flying at high altitudes, it was a natural for the Merlin XX and its derivatives. Early Mosquitoes were powered by single-stage Merlin 20 series engines, while later models were fitted with two-stage Merlin 60s and 70s. Mosquitoes built in Canada were powered by Packard-built Merlins, and the last production variants of the Mosquito, the Marks 34, 35 and 36, were fitted with the Merlin 113 and 114 engines which delivered 1,430 bhp at 27,250 feet, with a boost pressure of plus 18 lb. Over 7,700 Mosquitoes were built.

Ronnie Harker described the Mosquito as 'a most versatile aeroplane and a mix of bombs, guns, rockets and long-range fuel tanks' which could be fitted according to the task in hand. (He could have added cameras, used for PR purposes, and flares, used in Pathfinder sorties.) He wrote later:

They even flew to neutral Sweden to pick up ball bearings which, for a time, were in very short supply in England. For the latter operation they were painted in British Overseas Airways Corporation colours and were flown by airline pilots, even a passenger being sometimes carried in a bomb bay! At times, the Mosquitoes were intercepted by Focke-Wulf 190s but they were able to outpace them; none were lost.

With the 23,000 Spitfires and 14,500 Hurricanes, we can see that the demand for Merlin engines was heavy and constant.

THE SUPERCHARGER

In improving the performance of the Merlin engine – and therefore the performance of the Spitfires and Hurricanes – the supercharger was vital. We have already seen how the expert of the 1920s, Jimmy Ellor, was brought to Derby from the Royal Aircraft Establishment at Farnborough in late 1927 (with their blessing, it should be said). The man who developed the supercharger further in the late 1930s was Dr Stanley G. Hooker, later to become a key, if slightly controversial, figure within Rolls-Royce. His description of a supercharger in his book *Not much of an Engineer*, published by Airlife in 1984, is much better than anything we could achieve:

Briefly, a centrifugal supercharger consists of a rotor carrying a number of equally spaced radial vanes. In the case of the Merlin supercharger, which I was examining, the rotor was 10.25 in (260 mm) in diameter and had 16 vanes. It was driven by the engine through a step-up gear, and revolved at 28,000 rpm. The air entered at the centre of the rotor, moved out radially under the centrifugal force, and was flung off the rim into a stationary 12-vaned diffuser, the object of which was to convert the velocity of the air into the pressure which forced greater masses of air into the cylinders of the engine. If one thinks of the cylinders and pistons of an engine as the heart which converts the force of the burning air and petrol mixture into mechanical power by the downward motion of the piston, then the supercharger is the lungs of the engine, and by its efficiency controls the power output.

Clearly, the efficiency of the supercharger depends upon the efficiency of its component parts – the rotor and the diffuser – and to get the best results the maximum efficiency of the rotor must be made to coincide with the maximum efficiency of the diffuser. I found, by mathematical analysis and much to my surprise, that this happy coincidence did not occur on the Merlin supercharger, and that changes to both the rotor and diffuser were necessary. I even computed that the efficiency of the supercharger would improve from the existing 65 per cent to a new level of 75 per cent by such changes, but could it be true? How could the great Rolls-Royce firm have missed this?

Conscious that he might have made a mistake, Hooker checked and rechecked his calculations. He then sent a report to A.G. Elliott, who said that he would send it on to the accepted expert, Jimmy Ellor. After a number of days, Ellor arrived in Hooker's office with the report in his hand, and said: 'Did you write this?' Hooker replied nervously that he had. 'Well done, jolly good stuff', said Ellor. 'From now on you are in charge of supercharger development.'

Hooker began to make improvements which were incorporated into what became the Merlin XX and 45 for Spitfires and the Merlin XX for Hurricanes, Mosquitoes and Lancasters. As Hooker put it, 'For me the impossible had come to pass. I had changed an engine designed by the great Henry Royce himself.'

Although Hooker was to receive most of the credit for the supercharger which gave the Merlin its vital extra performance, it is very important not to forget the contribution made by Jimmy Ellor. And Hooker himself acknowledged this contribution, writing: 'This work is a continuation and amplification of that begun under the direction of Mr. J.E. Ellor.'

The Merlin XX, first produced in July 1940, and the Merlin 45, first produced in January 1941, increased the full-throttle altitude of the engine from 16,000 feet with the Merlin III to over 19,000 feet with the Merlin 45.

But development did not stop there. Everyone knew that the Germans would be constantly improving the performance of their engines and aircraft. The British must try to outguess them and stay ahead. And it was not only by refinements to the supercharger that the power of the Merlin could be improved. Fuel quality was also important. As Hooker pointed out:

There was another vital reason for keeping the boost pressure constant at a predetermined value, and this was the need to prevent the engine detonating. The ideal situation is that the charge of fuel and air should burn smoothly in the cylinders. If too much charge is forced in by too high a boost pressure from the supercharger, then detonation can begin and, instead of burning smoothly, the charge literally explodes, and causes shockwaves, like those at the nose of bullets, to bounce around inside the cylinders. These waves are of such intensity that serious mechanical damage can be caused to the cylinder head and pistons, which for lightness are made of aluminium, and thus can be relatively easily damaged.

The onset of detonation can be controlled by the octane value of the fuel, which in 1939 was limited to 87. Just before the Battle of Britain, small amounts of 100-octane fuel became available from the USA and this enabled us to open the throttle further on the Merlin and, in fact, to obtain nearly 2,000 hp without detonation. Thus, the 100-octane fuel made a crucial contribution to the performance of the Spitfire and Hurricane in that battle, as did the work of Lovesey, Rubbra, and their teams, which enabled the Merlin to withstand double its design power for short periods without mechanical failure.

To obtain the increased power, the pilot had to override the boost control which was normally limiting him to 1,000 hp. To do this, he had to pull a knob in the cockpit, and break the seal on it. So we always knew when he had done it! But in the Battle of Britain, 1,000 ft of extra altitude or 5 mph in speed could mean the difference between shooting down the enemy or being shot down by him, such was the equality between the performances of the Bf 109 and our fighters.

Thus, with the advent of 100-octane fuel, we were for the time being released from the nightmares of detonation. We could concentrate on improving the mechanical integrity of the Merlin to withstand higher power, which was Lovesey's job, and improving the performance of the supercharger so that the power could be increased and also maintained to higher and higher altitudes, which was my job.

The next big leap forward in performance stemmed from development work carried out by Hooker and his team on behalf of the Air Ministry. Rex Pierson, the chief designer at Vickers, had designed a capsule which fitted into the nose of the Wellington bomber in which the pilot and the bomb-aimer could sit. Pierson's idea was to pressurise the capsule so that the aircraft could fly above 30,000 feet. The Wellington's standard engine was a Bristol Hercules sleeve-valve radial. To boost its power to get the Wellington above 30,000 feet, Bristol had decided to fit an exhaust-driven turbosupercharger, similar to the ones being used by the Americans on their air-cooled engines. The Air Ministry considered this Wellington project so important that they wanted Rolls-Royce to turbocharge a Merlin as insurance.

Barnes Wallis, later to become immortalised by his 'bouncing bomb' (used successfully in the Dam Busters raid on the Mohne and Eder dams in Germany on the night of 16–17 May 1943), had been working at Vickers as a designer, and had convinced Beaverbrook of the possibility and efficacy of flying bombers at high altitude. Beaverbrook became determined to equip the RAF with such a weapon, and on 9 January 1941 he wrote to Vickers:

High-altitude bombers are to be developed intensively. I wish you to undertake this work. The Wellington V is to be fully developed with Hercules and Merlin engines. The Merlin is to take preference.

As Hooker pointed out, this was not going to be easy. Ray Dorey and Harry Pearson had already carried out a great deal of work at Hucknall on the Spitfire and Hurricane, taking the exhaust from the Merlin and ejecting it backwards through very short exhaust pipes where it acted as a means of jet propulsion equivalent to about an extra 150 hp. With an exhaust-driven turbocharger, that effect would be lost. Hooker argued that to raise the necessary power the full-throttle height of the Merlin should be raised from 16,000 to 30,000 feet by putting two superchargers in series at the back of the engine, driven by the same gears already fitted to the standard Merlin.

However, there was a snag to this suggestion. Because of the high compression of the charge, the temperature would soar and the old problem of detonation would return. The solution was to add an extra liquid-cooled 'intercooler', which would cool the charge to 100 degrees centigrade before it entered the cylinders. Desk-top calculations showed that by this method the power of the Merlin at 30,000 feet could be doubled from 500 to 1,000 hp. All that they had to do was determine the size of the two superchargers. Within months, after experiments with both the Merlin and Vulture superchargers, and with help on the intercooler from the RAE, Rolls-Royce had an engine ready for testing. It worked well on the test-bed, and shortly afterwards two engines were installed in a Wellington at Hucknall. On its first flight, the Wellington reached 29,750 feet – clearly the experiment had worked.

But Hives was not satisfied with that, and asked: 'What would happen if we put it in the Spitfire?' It was an obvious idea, though it does not appear to have occurred to anyone else. It would, however, require considerable modification to the aircraft, because this engine was nine inches longer than the standard Merlin. The whole of the nose, including the engine mounting and controls, would have to be re-designed.

A new four-blade propeller would be needed to convert the power into thrust, and an extra radiator under the wing would be needed to dissipate the heat in the coolant that cooled the charge. However, all this was achieved, and in 1941 a Spitfire flew with this Merlin 61 engine, reaching a height of 40,000 feet.

This was the prototype of the famous Spitfire IX. The new Merlin 61 had increased its fighting altitude by 10,000 feet and its top speed by 70 mph, and it arrived in the sky just in time to do battle with the Focke-Wulf 190. Hooker related in his book that Harry (later to become Air Marshal Sir Harry) Broadhurst, one of the country's leading fighter pilots, told him that he had seen the look of astonishment on a German pilot's face as he climbed past him in a Spitfire IX.

Ironically, the Wellington bomber with the pressurised cabin never went into service, but the new Merlin went into mass-production and was fitted into Spitfires, P-51 Mustangs and Mosquitoes. It proved outstandingly successful in the Mustang, which in Hooker's words 'was the only aircraft that really challenged the supreme performance of the Spitfire'.

RADAR, PROPELLERS AND FUEL

It is impossible to write about the Merlin and the power and performance it gave which enabled the RAF to gain mastery of the skies without mentioning three other ingredients contributing to that success.

The first was Radar (Radio Detection And Ranging). The British began their experiments with radar in 1935, and although the Germans were ahead by a year, in the practical use of this new science the British excelled themselves. In close co-operation with Dowding, the civil servant Henry (later Sir Henry) Tizard created the radar network that made it possible to anticipate – and therefore have time to get into the position to defeat – the bomber attacks of the Luftwaffe in 1940.

A committee had been set up by the British Government in 1934, under Tizard, to consider possible means of defence against the bomber. Robert (later Sir Robert) Watson-Watt, a slightly overweight scientist at the National Physical Laboratory, was asked to investigate the possibility of a 'death ray'. Watson-Watt and his assistant, Arnold 'Skip' Wilkins, dismissed this idea, since no aircraft would linger in the most intense beam of radio energy that the scientists could produce for long enough to knock out its engine. However, they suggested three areas worthy of investigation: the redirection of radio-waves to detect aircraft; radio-telephone communication between a ground controller and defending fighters to direct them to the aircraft located; and a coded signal from friendly aircraft to distinguish them from enemy aircraft.

Watson-Watt later received the credit for the development of radar to a usable state, but it was his assistant Wilkins who had recalled how Post Office engineers complained that radio reception was disturbed when aircraft flew close to their receivers. He thought: 'Might not an aircraft's electromagnetic energy be visually depicted by use of the cathode-ray apparatus?'

This information was considered by the Tizard Committee when it met at the end of January 1935, and on 26 February the first practical test took place. A van containing suitable radio receivers stationed itself in a field about ten miles from the short-wave transmitters of the Daventry broadcasting stations. A pilot flew over a course near the radio station, and the van's instruments detected the aircraft. Such a simple but successful experiment prompted Tizard and Dowding to support Watson-Watt, who took a team to Bawdsey Manor on the Suffolk coast to develop the system further.

By the late 1930s, other nations (including Germany, France, Holland and the USA) had reached a similar state of development, but Germany, anticipating a short war and rapid peace negotiations with Britain, did not see the necessity for its use in defence, and also failed to appreciate its usefulness in Britain's protection of itself. When the war came, the Luftwaffe never attacked the radar stations in a concerted way. Neither France nor the USA seemed to appreciate radar's military usefulness.

Two factors were essential for the successful use of the early warning system. One was the speed with which the radar information was transmitted, and the other was the continued observation of an enemy aircraft's track and the ability to transmit this information to fighter groups. Major Adolf 'Dolfo' Galland, one of the Luftwaffe's fighter aces, was to say later:

In battle we had to rely on our own eyes. The British fighter pilots could depend on the radar eye, which was far more reliable and had a longer range. When we made contact with the enemy our briefings were already three hours old, the British only as many seconds old – the time it took to assess the latest position by means of radar to the transmission of orders to the force in the air.

'Stuffy' Dowding said:

Where would we have been without RDF [radar] and all that went with it? We could never have maintained the vast number of standing patrols that would have been necessary if we had not had that magic sight.

Another development that was to prove of critical importance in the coming conflict was the variable pitch propeller. On the fighters and bombers of the First World War, the propeller (or airscrew as it was often called in those days) was carved from wood and had a fixed pitch. Even at that stage it was appreciated that a propeller whose pitch could be varied for differing engine speeds would give greater performance. In the second half of 1917, a four-bladed propeller with variable pitch was made and tested at the Royal Aircraft Factory, and in 1918 a two-bladed version was fitted to an SE5. At this time, the variation in pitch was achieved manually by the pilot, but this was clearly not satisfactory and in the mid-1920s Dr H.S. Hele-Shaw and T.E. Beacham patented a hydraulic device. At the same time, some urgency was given to the development of variable pitch propellers by the increased power generated by supercharged engines. In 1925, tenders for an all-metal variable pitch propeller were invited by the Air Ministry, and in August of that year tests were carried out at RAE Farnborough. Following these tests, a contract for twelve propellers was given to the Gloster Aircraft Company. Two propellers were developed and flown in 1928, one with hollow steel blades fitted to a Rolls-Royce Kestrel engine, and the other with solid duralumin blades to a Bristol Jupiter engine. The pitch range was about twelve degrees.

Hollow blades proved unsatisfactory and, under licence from the Gloster company, Rolls-Royce and Bristol sought to find an alternative. In the meantime, in the USA, the Hamilton Hydraulic Airscrew Company applied for a patent for a two-position propeller in May 1929. By 1934, the Hamilton propeller was in production, and de Havilland acquired a licence from Hamilton.

By 1939, nine out of every ten Mercury and Pegasus engines manufactured by the Bristol Aircraft Company were fitted with de Havilland propellers which were made under licence from Hamilton. At the same time, the German propeller manufacturers had also mastered the design and production of variable pitch propellers.

Roy Fedden, chief engineer of the engine department of the Bristol Aircraft Company (BAC), had become convinced of the need for variable pitch propellers if the new fighters were to achieve their full potential, and he was dismayed by the slowness of development. After trying unsuccessfully to persuade his Bristol board, he was instrumental in persuading de Havilland to take the Hamilton licence. But he was not satisfied with having a competitor as the only producer, and so he went to the Air Ministry. Air Marshal Dowding asked him to produce two propellers to the Hele-Shaw/Beacham design.

Dowding also asked Rolls-Royce to produce some prototypes, and they approached the construction in a different way. While Bristol used a cylinder with radial pins sliding inside the forged steel hub, the Rolls-Royce design used a fixed inner piston carrying an external sliding cylinder which drove the blades by push-pull rods.

But Fedden did not want two versions of the Hele-Shaw to compete with the Hamilton and, in a commercially unconventional and patriotic gesture, he approached his major competitor, Rolls-Royce, inviting Managing Director Arthur Sidgreaves and Ernest Hives to lunch at the Royal Thames Yacht Club. The three reached agreement that a joint venture was necessary and would be successful. At this point, the idea received the blessing of the BAC board and the Air Ministry. On 13 May 1937, Rotol Airscrews Limited was formed. (The name comes from 'RO' of Rolls-Royce and 'TOL' of Bristol, and was apparently the idea of the wife of Bill Stammers, the first General Manager.) The prospectus of the new company, based in Gloucester with a nominal capital of £250,000 (perhaps £12.5 million in today's terms), stated:

Although the main production of Rotol Airscrews Ltd. will be of the hydraulically operated type, the electrically operated airscrew will also be made and is a development of the well-known Curtiss-Wright airscrew of the USA, particularly suitable for heavy multi-engined machines as it can be 'feathered'. Initially all propellers will have magnesium blades, but the company will conduct developments with blades of wood and other materials.

The first Rotol propeller was made in the Derby Experimental Department and tested on a Merlin in the original hangar on Sinfin Moor, now the site of Rolls-Royce's main offices. If the variable pitch propeller was a key factor, many have claimed that the Battle of Britain would have been lost but for the use of 100 octane fuel in the Merlins. Indeed, no less a figure than Air Chief Marshal Lord Tedder listed the fuel as one of the three deciding factors in the battle.

By 1937, the British Air Ministry, convinced that 100 octane fuel (developed and tested by the US Army Air Force) could boost the power of aero engines, began importing small quantities and sending them to Rolls-Royce for testing in the Merlin, to Bristol for testing in the Pegasus and to RAE Farnborough for testing in single-cylinder test engines. The Air Ministry was probably influenced by a paper given by Rod Banks (at that time employed by the Ethyl Corporation) to the Royal Aeronautical Society and the Institute of Petroleum on

8 January 1937, in which he said that the RAF should be supplied with engines that could use 100 octane fuel 'even if the supply of such fuel were limited, because the use of high-duty equipment might prove decisive in the early stages of a war'. The Ethyl Corporation carried out continuous research into the effectiveness of various fuels, and Rod Banks made sure that any developments were passed on to the British engine manufacturers.

The first full cargo of 'BAM100' (British Air Ministry 100 octane fuel) was shipped in June 1939 from the Esso refinery in Aruba. The Air Ministry began to stockpile subsequent shipments, while in the meantime the RAF continued to use its standard 87 octane. Most shipments came from Esso and Shell refineries in the USA, but fortunately some came from Aruba and Curacao for, when war was declared on 3 September 1939, the US Congress invoked the Neutrality Act prohibiting the export of strategic materials to belligerent nations.

In the first half of 1940, the RAF transferred all Hurricane and Spitfire squadrons to 100 octane fuel. The effect was described by Bill Gunston in *Rolls-Royce, Aero Engines*:

Instead of being limited to a maximum of 6 lb/sq in boost, pilots could 'go through the gate' to full throttle and 12 lb boost, thus increasing the power of the Merlin II or III from approximately 1,000 hp to 1,310. This 30% power increase made a significant improvement to take-off, rate of climb and maximum speed up to about 9,000 ft, above which boost had to fall away. The new fuel really came into its own on the central-entry blower Merlin XX and 45, which could maintain 12 lb up to fighting altitudes around 20,000 ft. Even so, the difference 100-octane made to the Battle of Britain Merlins was very important, in a closely fought campaign.

The importance of 100/130 fuel was underlined by other factors. The Luftwaffe's standard single-seat fighter, the Bf 109E, was much lighter than either the Hurricane or Spitfire, and it was powered by an engine of 25% greater capacity (2069 cu in compared with the Merlin's 1,649). As there was not much difference in weight between the two engines, it was imperative for Rolls-Royce to develop the Merlin both to tolerate higher manifold pressure for more power at low altitudes and, especially, superior supercharging for greater power at high altitudes. It is a truly amazing fact that Rolls-Royce succeeded on both counts, and kept the Merlin consistently ahead of the larger DB 601 and later DB 605 right to the end of the war. Another factor emphasising the need for 100/130 fuel was that, until the start of the Battle of Britain, large numbers of Hurricanes and Spitfires still had the Merlin II driving crude two-blade wooden fixed-pitch propellers, whereas every Bf 109E had the constant-speed VDM [electrically actuated propeller pitch control].

CHAPTER SIX

PRIORITIES

'WE TAKE NO NOTICE OF THEM'
'THE BETTER IS THE ENEMY OF THE GOOD'
NOT THE ENGINE REQUIRED FOR THIS WAR

'WE TAKE NO NOTICE OF THEM'

While Hives was coping with all the problems of trying to increase production of the Merlin while at the same time maintaining the necessary quality, he felt moved to complain to Beaverbrook that conflicting statements issued by various ministries were making the task of management unnecessarily difficult. He quoted the following examples to the Minister:

(1) The Prime Minister states the Air Force is growing stronger every day.
(2) The Minister of Aircraft Production states that he has been able to replace all casualties by the repair of the aircraft.
(3) The Minister of Labour states that the workers should have rest periods.
(4) The Minister of Health complains because we are working our female dilutees more than the recognised hours.
(5) The medical profession will always say a man requires a holiday if they know he is working at Rolls-Royce.

We are spending our time trying to explain that the Ministers don't mean what they say and that there is a dangerous shortage of aircraft.

We are not at all impressed by the M.A.P.'s propaganda in the factories. A Conservative M.P. does not impress our workers one little bit. We could do infinitely better ourselves. It needs someone who understands the psychology of the workers ... We quite understand that the national propaganda will have to be adapted to suit its own peculiar conditions. As we are fighting for the national freedom of the individual we cannot use force, so we must rely on the right kind of appeal and our contention is that so far this has not been made.

He suggested, as an example of the type of appeal which would have some effect, that some of the women who had been bombed out in London should be sent round the aircraft factories. These suggestions did not fall on deaf ears. Beaverbrook replied that he was grateful for this criticism which he considered would have a most beneficial effect. A few days later Hives visited London to discuss engine policy with him and saw some of the results of the bombing for himself. On his return to Derby he immediately arranged for four members of the Shop Committee to go up to London by car.

In a report to the board, Hives summarised the results of his discussions with the Minister. The Bristol factory had been hit and badly damaged and in consequence Lord Beaverbrook had decided that the main factories should disperse as much as possible to reduce their vulnerability. The RAF was now even more dependent than before on the Rolls-Royce factories. It did not take the Government long to discover, however, that the psychological effects of bombing were both more dangerous and less predictable than the physical. In 1940 the Luftwaffe was concentrating all its power on defeating the RAF and on destroying the morale of the British people. Industrial destruction was fitted into this pattern wherever possible and convenient. 'Results have shown', said Hives, 'that bombing has not destroyed any considerable number of machine tools. The thing it does destroy is the morale of the workers, and this is very difficult to restore ... Our instructions are to disperse as much as we can ... I spent two hours with Lord Beaverbrook and he showed me all the confidential reports. There is one thing which has no need to be kept secret as far as we are concerned, and that is that we are not producing nearly enough engines. We must produce more and we want them at once.'

The great increase in production which had been achieved at both factories in the summer and autumn was not maintained during the last few months of the year, the total output declining from 778 in October to 606 in December. It had recovered to 920 by March 1941, but the average in the first six months of 1941, during which the first complete engines from Glasgow began to come in, remained at 785. The total number of engines produced during this period was 4,710, the total number absorbed into airframes 4,137. In February, however, output was exceeded by absorption for the first time. This figure (785) was 300 in excess of the output expected in the last pre-war programme (11 August 1939), 129 in excess of that demanded by the 29 March 1940 programme, 559 below that demanded by the 26 July programme and 485 below that expected in a programme issued on 7 March 1941 (for which the calculations were presumably made before February). The error in these estimates was thus substantial. This was partly due to the change in type from the Merlin III and X to the Merlin XX. The Merlin X was similar to the Merlin III (which was almost identical to the Merlin II) except for a different reduction gear ratio and a Farman-type supercharger drive. This had been developed when difficulties were experienced with a more novel type of two-speed supercharger on which work had been in progress since January 1935. These were the Merlins with which the RAF entered the war.

The next important modification was the introduction of a pressurised cooling system using only 30 per cent glycol, which first appeared in a small number of Merlin IVs and which came into production in September 1939 on the Merlin XII. It was also due to the effort which was being made at Derby to bring the Vulture into production. The MAP programmes were little more than extravagant hopes which made little allowance for the many vicissitudes of war production and there was no escaping the fact that the production of the Merlin XX was at a dangerously low level.

Hives was well aware of this and he immediately set about analysing the causes of the failure. The MAP programmes were based largely on the firm's own estimates of production and Rolls-Royce officials had been persuaded to set these unduly high towards the latter part of 1940. The methods of the MAP were well known and it was felt that since their programmes would make little difference to the output actually obtained, if the Air Ministry and MAP insisted on unrealistic and optimistic estimates, the easiest thing to do was to provide them! Lord Beaverbrook himself was largely responsible for the insistence of the MAP that unrealistic programmes should not be altered downwards. On 3 December 1940 he had told the heads of the various production departments that the programmes must stand, 'damage or no damage'. This statement shows quite clearly that he was using the programme as a psychological device rather than as an instrument of measurement or control. As a psychological device the target programme has grave weaknesses, especially when, as was the case in December 1940, the psychological maxima have already been reached. There were no responsible officials either at the MAP or in the firms who did not realise that a maximum effort was demanded. But there were many people who, for a variety of reasons, had no very clear idea of how this maximum effort could best be directed.

In a report on the general state of engine production throughout the group written on 17 December 1940 Hives maintained that output was still in excess of absorption, although he expected the latter to increase. 'According to Air Ministry programmes', he added, 'we are several hundred engines in debt, but from experience we know that all Air Ministry programmes are at least 30 per cent higher than is ever obtained.' In due course Lord Beaverbrook agreed to scale the programmes down to figures which were more reasonable. The production target of all types of aircraft by December 1941 laid down in the October 1940 programme was reduced from 2,782 to 2,221 per month. The bombing of the British Thomson-Houston magneto works, which had considerable repercussions on the output of complete engines, was mainly responsible for this decision.

Late in December Hives visited Sir Patrick Hennessy, Lord Beaverbrook's personal assistant at the MAP, to discuss the whole subject of programming. As a result of this discussion he again recommended that Rolls-Royce should supply the aircraft manufacturers directly.

Everyone knows that the collection of figures which are sent out in the present Air Ministry provisioning programmes don't mean anything. We take no notice of them.

The only way we are able to meet the varying demands as regards types and quantities is by direct contact with the consumer (aircraft constructor) which is confirmed by our own representatives who are permanently resident at each of the aircraft constructors. Our proposal is that this method should be officially recognised by the M.A.P. and adopted as a basis of engine production programmes. All we ask is that Rolls-Royce should receive every month from each of the aircraft constructors who are using our engines a statement showing their requirements ... Looking at the figures for the number of Rolls-Royce engines required this year which are on the Air Ministry programme, it is certain that we can never produce them by a considerable margin. At the same time we are confident that we can meet all the requirements.

The Ministry would not agree to this proposal since it would have meant abandoning the comforting illusion that the programmes controlled the output of engines. There were other good reasons for requiring the engine firms to produce an output in excess of that which the demands of aircraft constructors alone would have brought forth, but these do not seem ever to have been clearly set out for the benefit of those who were endeavouring to operate under the programme regime.

These reasons were that surplus engines were required to cover:

1. Engines required in transit to manufacturers and squadrons.

2. Stocks maintained at squadrons.
3. The completion of older marks of aircraft which were not adaptable to newer marks of engine which might have come into production before the airframe programme had been completed.
4. The provision of a stock of engines as an insurance against bombing.

The real reasons for the failure of production to rise must be sought elsewhere. When, early in 1940, the Air Staff had discussed the trends of German production and development they had reached the conclusion that the RAF was in danger of losing the technical superiority, especially of its fighters, with which it entered the war and which had proved of such immense importance during the Battle of Britain. It was felt that this could be maintained only by bringing into production new types of higher-powered engine and in this respect the Rolls-Royce Vulture and the Napier Sabre were looked upon as the logical successors to the Merlin. The Vulture was intended for the Avro Manchester twin-engined heavy bomber and the Sabre for the Hawker Typhoon. The Vulture was abandoned before its development had been completed because of Hives's insistence that Rolls-Royce should concentrate on the Merlin and Griffon. The Sabre's development was so slow that when it finally did come into production the purpose for which it had originally been designed had been fulfilled by other engines. Throughout 1941 the Air Ministry and the MAP were unable to formulate a clear policy on these two engines and at one stage it was uncertain whether the development of the Sabre would be handed over to Rolls-Royce or the Glasgow factory turned over to the production of the Sabre. Both proposals were seriously considered.

'THE BETTER IS THE ENEMY OF THE GOOD'

In June 1940 Hives advised Sir Wilfrid Freeman that it would be in the best interests of the RAF to produce the Merlin rather than the Vulture or Sabre. His main argument was that

146

these 24-cylinder engines were not installationally inter-changeable with the Merlin and that if the factory producing either engine were to be bombed the Merlin could not be used in their place, with the result that new aircraft would be grounded without engines. As a result of the order suspending development work after Dunkirk and the impairment in the co-ordination of policy on design and development between the MAP and the Air Ministry which took place under Lord Beaverbrook, the situation became increasingly confused towards the end of 1940. This confusion produced a crop of wild schemes and rumours which did not disappear until the Joint Production and Development Committee under the Chairmanship of Sir Henry Tizard was established. The return of Sir Wilfrid Freeman from the MAP to the Air Ministry, where he was no longer able to maintain such close contact with the firms, had a great deal to do with the blurring of policy which was evident at this time.

On 9 October the Rolls-Royce Chairman, Lord Herbert Scott, wrote to Sidgreaves expressing great concern over the propaganda which was being developed about the relative merits of the Sabre and the Vulture. He foresaw the danger that the authorities, the Air Force and the pilots would become divided into two camps, and suggested that this would not be in the best interests of the war effort. He concluded with a somewhat drastic suggestion. 'From a national and company point of view we should do all we can to prevent Napier going into full production ... It is a dangerous policy to change horses crossing a river.' Lord Herbert Scott suspected that the boost which was being given to the Sabre had financial implications, and his long association with Rolls-Royce and his experience of the type of inter-company politics which characterised the First World War inclined him to take a somewhat narrow point of view on the subject.

Hives needed no reminding of the dangers in the Sabre/Vulture policy, but he refused to lend his authority to political manoeuvres of this description, following the clear precedent which Claude Johnson had established in the First World War. 'I thought', he commented in a minute to Sidgreaves, 'it

147

had been accepted that the only thing that mattered was to win the war and that the question of commercial prestige was to be forgotten in the present struggle. Considering that the country is purchasing thousands of aero-engines from the U.S.A. I do not see how we could justify any endeavour to prevent the Sabre engine going into production ... The answer to the Sabre is for us to show that the Vulture is the better engine. That is the only thing that counts in the end.'

The problem was nevertheless of national proportions since the decision involved the allocation of the resources of a major part of the aero engine capacity in the country, in particular the No. 1 Shadow Group which was about to complete its Pegasus and Mercury contracts. The Centaurus, Griffon, Sabre and Vulture were the candidates for production in these factories and in August 1941 it was decided to allot 75 per cent of the capacity of the group to the Sabre at a conversion cost alone of over £3 million. The Vulture was rejected because of its failure on the Manchester, and the Griffon because of its relatively undeveloped state and the burden which the technical parentage of an outside group of factories would have imposed on the Rolls-Royce management. Within a few months the failure of the Sabre engine made it necessary to reverse this decision and switch the whole group on to the Bristol Hercules engine.

Hives took a serious view of the possibilities of using different engines, some of them not made by Rolls-Royce, and in October 1940 he expressed his doubts in a lengthy memorandum to Lord Beaverbrook, claiming that: 'Most of the Rolls-Royce successes have been achieved when we have acted contrary to the official recommendations.'

Hives felt that he could place little faith in reports that wonderful new aircraft were about to take to the air. 'The policy should be', he suggested, to make the Hurricane and Spitfire 'as good as we know how to make them.' The Hurricane with the Merlin XX had a greatly improved performance and the output of the Merlin XX could be greatly increased if orders for the Merlin III were reduced. In conclusion he argued that it was absurd to expect any contribution from the

Sabre Typhoon during 1941. 'A Rolls-Royce quotation is that one machine in the air is worth an infinite number on the drawing board, in the workshops or on the ground.'

Beaverbrook replied immediately in a short note saying that, as usual, he welcomed criticism 'bearing in mind always the need for brevity and in terms that will enable us to reach conclusions rather than delve into reasons for errors and mistakes in the past'. A short while later he replied in greater detail. 'I hope', he said, 'Mr Hives and Mr Sidgreaves may continue to watch the rise and fall of Ministers for the next twenty-five years. And if this Minister should fall shortly he will not break his heart on that account.' He agreed that the Merlin was an undoubted success but he thought that Rolls-Royce were being inhuman in not condoning the expression of hope and enthusiasm for new engines. 'The publicity that goes on about new types is inherent in the heart of man. It will be with us as long as there is hope in the land.' This was an old argument in a new guise. Beaverbrook's principal tasks were to generate enthusiasm and a sense of urgency. Hives's argument was that wishful thinking should be discouraged if it led to wishful action that ignored the warnings of experience. In another section of his report he had commented that the aircraft industry was often tempted to regard production of service machines as 'an engineering hobby instead of as a means of waging war'. Hives thought that the MAP might be succumbing to this temptation where the Vulture and Sabre were concerned. 'The proverb the better is the enemy of the good, especially when the better does not exist, applies very much to the aircraft programme.' Beaverbrook replied that he did not understand the meaning of this paragraph. 'But then', he added, with a mischievous flourish, 'I have never been able to deal with temptation.'

NOT THE ENGINE REQUIRED FOR THIS WAR

Another serious criticism in Hives and Sidgreaves's report referred to the confusion which existed on the subject of the Merlin-engined Wellington. The position of this aircraft had never been made clear despite the fact that its bomb-load capacity was far greater than that of the Pegasus-engined machine. In his reply to this memorandum the Minister instructed that the production of the Merlin X for the Wellington should continue and that the production of Merlin XXs should be increased though not at the expense of a decline in total output. The Vulture and the Griffon were to be brought on as swiftly as possible.

These instructions did not greatly clarify the issue. The order to increase Merlin XX production but 'not at the expense of total output' is a good example of the type of order which appears on the surface to be quite reasonable, especially to the executor, but which to the executee immediately begs a whole series of questions if it is not to be interpreted as a mere platitude. Some of the requests for information which were received indicated clearly that the reorganisation at the MAP had left some officials high and dry on islands of paper which were quite isolated from the mainland of the industry. On 27 July, more than a year after production had started at Crewe, the following telegram was received from the MAP.

Re Crewe Merlin and Glasgow wire anticipated date completion of buildings and plant and when production partial or otherwise can commence. A.P.E. Air-minded Harrogate.

This was ignored, though it caused much amusement. It was followed a month later by a further telegram.

A.P.E. 291 27/8 Wire briefly or write by return if possible progress plant and machine tools, when installation commenced or when expected start. What items holding up installation of balanced unit percentage plant in production. Production labour at work as a percentage total labour required full production. D.A.P.F.6.

Copies of these telegrams, with the request that the author should be discovered, were sent to R.H. Coverley, Director of Engine Production at the Air Ministry, with Hives's comment: 'We have started a form-filling-in department for the Ministry of Labour, the Ministry of Health and the M.A.P. but Mr D.A.P.F.6 we propose to ignore.'

During the latter part of 1940, mainly because of the changes in personnel which had taken place at both Ministries during the year, the relationship between the company and the Ministries deteriorated slightly and in consequence both sides were inclined to blame each other for the misunderstandings which arose chiefly from ineffective communication. A channel of communication which exists in theory but which is in practice closed by a conflict or lack of sympathy between individuals is not an effective channel, and there were many instances, both within the organisation of the group and between the management and the Ministries, where the paramount importance of friendly personal contact as an instrument of effective administration was made abundantly clear. The efficacy of a formal pattern of administrative organisation depends almost entirely on the informal organisation which develops within it, and which may in no way resemble it. The latter cannot be created quickly and it is easily destroyed if the turnover of personnel is too rapid. It is also more important where, as in the case of higher policy decisions, the element of mutual confidence is vital. This state of affairs is clearly revealed in comments which Hives made on the general state of engine production in the group at the end of December 1940. 'We are finding it terribly difficult in dealing with M.A.P.', he said, 'because the whole of the staff who were responsible for the building up of our present Air Force have now disappeared and have not so far been replaced.' For this reason, as much as any other, his advocacy of the continued development of the Spitfire and Hurricane was sometimes suspected of being partisan by those who regarded all problems in terms of an irreconcilable conflict between private profit and the public interest, a bogus antithesis which has stultified many decisions.

At the end of 1940 Rolls-Royce was still committed to the production of the Vulture. Eighty-eight of these engines were produced in 1940 and 337 in 1941. It was not until March 1942 that production ceased altogether. Early in 1941 Hives had told Sir Patrick Hennessy that although Vulture engines were giving excellent service in Manchester squadrons Rolls-Royce was confident that the four-Merlined Lancaster would prove the better machine. 'We are not', he wrote, 'seeking orders for the Vulture – our anxiety is that the M.A.P. will be inviting disaster if the figures for 1942 are to be dependent on a new type of engine.' MAP seemed to have no clear policy for the Vulture at this time and Lord Beaverbrook, to whom Hives had complained that a clear decision one way or another was necessary, suggested that he would give Rolls-Royce a production order for at least 500 engines when the engine had achieved a specified performance in the Tornado airframe. Hives thought that there would be no difficulty in achieving this but he was convinced that the same production and development effort expended on the Merlin would bring far better results. In a strong memorandum to Sir Charles Craven written on 26 April he accused the MAP of being more interested in producing novelties than in producing the maximum number of fighter or bomber aircraft and he suggested that the correct policy was to lay down that a given output of aircraft should be produced in a given period and that the introduction of new types should not be allowed to interfere with this. The MAP was far too susceptible to foolish promises and he argued that it would be little short of criminal to change production over to new types of fighter in 1942. Again and again in 1941 Hives pressed home the argument that 'the only thing to bank on for quantity production for next year is something which exists today'. A few months earlier he had used these arguments to influence Sabre policy. Now it was the Vulture and the Whittle XII which were hypnotising the Ministry. The Sabre battle had been lost but Hives was particularly vehement in denouncing the Ministry's attempt to canvass some of Rolls-Royce's best sub-contractors to make Sabre parts. But the battle over the Vulture had been won.

The Chief of Air Staff finally concurred with this point of view on the Tornado and Typhoon, and Rolls-Royce was instructed to make the maximum production effort on the high-altitude Merlin then in production and to bring on the two-stage engines then under development as fast as possible. Hives also had no faith in the basic design of the Typhoon-Tornado airframe, as he had occasion to point out to Air Marshal F.J. Linnell who was in charge of Research and Development at the Air Ministry. The M.109F – a fully operational aircraft of the Luftwaffe – had a better all-round performance than either the Typhoon or the Tornado, both of which had been designed before the war when no one had foreseen the likelihood of the enemy operating from bases just across the Channel. In addition both aircraft were uneconomical from the production point of view. Hives estimated that at least two 109Fs could be produced with the labour and material required for the Tornado or Typhoon. He also disagreed with the contention that since the Air Staff had decided to develop the Merlin- and Griffon-engined Spitfires for high-altitude work two classes of fighter should be produced to operate in specialised roles. 'My answer to this', he said, is that the right type will always find itself in the wrong place.' There was little doubt that the pursuit of this policy would have resulted in a much lower output of fighter aircraft in 1942.

A series of unfortunate fatal accidents on Manchester aircraft, some due to the Vulture itself, for the undeveloped state of which Rolls-Royce did not attempt to disclaim responsibility, some due to defective operation of the airscrews, finally decided Hives to insist on the abandonment of the engine. On 5 October he informed Major Bulman that Rolls-Royce was prepared, in the national interest, to scrap the Vulture V, the mark then under development, despite the fact that most of the teething troubles had just about been overcome. 'We shall set out to show that the Spitfire fitted with the latest Merlin can be very considerably improved. This also applies to other machines fitted with Merlins. This is obviously a better contribution to the national effort than spending our technical energy in proving that the Vulture is a better engine than the Sabre, because if the Tornado and Typhoon go along in parallel this is inevitably what would happen.' A desperate shortage of Merlins had developed by the end of the year despite increasing production, and in view of the demands which were made on the Merlin and on Derby in the spring of 1942 it is fortunate that the MAP concurred with this suggestion. A few days later Sir Charles Craven informed Derby by telephone that it had been decided to stop the production of the Vulture Tornado. Later, in 1942, when Hives was asked by Group Captain Banks whether he considered the Vulture could have been developed into an effective engine he declared that there was no doubt whatever that it could have been developed into the best engine of its class. The decision to abandon the engine was not a light-hearted one for the firm, which had spent three years developing the engine, but it was taken because the conclusion had been reached that the Vulture 'was not the engine that was required for this war'. Hives refused, in response to an invitation to do so, to criticise the Sabre, which by the end of 1942 had proved a great disappointment to its supporters, but he concluded that had both engines been continued the result might well have been a grave national disaster. This was no exaggeration.

As late as June 1941 Hives was writing to his friend Wilfrid Freeman, by this time Vice-Chief of Air Staff:

I've never yet attended a meeting at M.A.P. that I have not left with a stomach ache and a feeling that it has been a waste of time ... Since we now have to go through the Civil Service routine, it is impossible to get any decisions ... The only safe thing to bank on in quantity for next year is something which exists today ... Hurricane Is and Spitfire Is, if converted to take Merlin 45s, or Merlin 66s ... can be as good as any of the front-line aircraft.

CHAPTER SEVEN

A FINE AND VERSATILE FIGHTER

P51S – TANK BUSTERS
TILLY SCHILLING
QUILL LIKED THE GRIFFON

P51S – TANK BUSTERS

The Mustang is as highly revered in the USA as the Spitfire and the Hurricane are in Britain. To an American, the P51 Mustang was *the* fighter of the Second World War.[*]

Initially, the Mustang, specified and ordered by the British Purchasing Commission in the USA in 1940 when it was seeking to find a fighter to add to the Hurricanes and Spitfires in Britain's offensive and defensive armoury, was powered by the Allison V1710 engine.

---

[*] I have to insert a personal story here. In the autumn of 1998 I went to see Steven Spielberg's film *Saving Private Ryan*, in a small cinema on 42nd Street in Manhattan. At the end, when Private Ryan, whose four brothers have all been killed, is about to be blown to pieces by a German tank, a Mustang roars in and puts the tank out of action. Private Ryan says, with great relief:

'Ah P51s, tank-busters!'

At which point I have to confess that I stood up in the cinema and announced to the startled audience:

'Yes, and with Rolls-Royce Merlin engines!'

(Peter Pugh)

This low-altitude-rated engine did not allow the Mustang's aerodynamic features to be fully exploited, and the aircraft was initially given only close-support duties, while the Spitfire remained the RAF's premier fighter.

However, on 29 April 1942, Wing Commander Ian Campbell-Orde, commanding officer of the Air Fighting Development Unit (AFDU) at Duxford, rang Ronnie Harker, the Rolls-Royce service-liaison pilot, and asked him if he would like to come and try this new aeroplane from the USA which, in his opinion, was the best to come from that country so far. This was how Harker remembered it when he wrote his book *Rolls-Royce from the Wings*, published by Oxford Illustrated Press in 1976:

The General took me to the aeroplane and showed me all around it, explaining as he did so some of the history of how the specification had originated. As I flew the Mustang, I felt that it had a number of desirable features which the current fighters lacked. I was particularly impressed by its large fuel capacity of 269 gallons on internal tanks. This was three times as much as the Spitfire. I also liked the six .5 heavy machine-guns mounted close inboard in the wings, the light and effective aileron control which gave a high rate of roll and perhaps most important of all, its low drag which gave it a very noticeable increase in top speed over both British and German contemporary fighters.

With the low full throttle height of the Allison engine its overall performance was adequate for Army operation and reconnaissance duties at low altitude. However, one saw immediately the possibility of the Mustang as an air-superiority and long-range penetration fighter – if only it could be fitted with our latest two-speed, two-stage supercharged Merlin. If this was successful, it could be the answer to both the Me 109 and the Focke-Wulf 190, thus providing certain qualities that the Spitfire lacked. I discussed this proposal with The General after my flight, and we agreed to put it up as a serious proposition.

On returning to Hucknall, I asked Witold Challier, our Polish performance expert, to estimate what the Mustang would do when fitted with a Merlin 61. He reported that there would be a greatly

25. A Merlin-powered Spitfire MK XII.

26. A two-stage Merlin in a Spitfire.

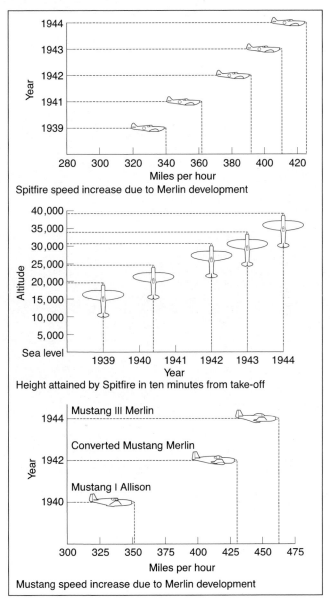

Spitfire speed increase due to Merlin development

Height attained by Spitfire in ten minutes from take-off

Mustang speed increase due to Merlin development

27. Charts showing the increase in performance
of the Spitfire thanks to the development of the Merlin.

28. A P51 Mustang of the USAF. This is a P51B in 1944

29. North American P51B Mustangs powered by Merlins.
Originally the Mustangs were fitted with Allison V-1710s but,
after Rolls-Royce liaison pilot Ronnie Harker tested
one at Duxford, it was recommended that both the RAF and
the USAF switch to Merlins.

30. The Rolls-Royce Griffon. At the beginning of 1939 Hives, already appreciating the need for a more powerful Merlin, ordered the development of a new Griffon to be interchangeable with the Merlin.

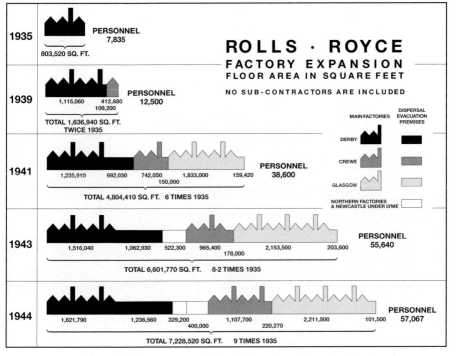

1935
803,520 SQ. FT.
PERSONNEL 7,835

ROLLS · ROYCE
FACTORY EXPANSION
FLOOR AREA IN SQUARE FEET
NO SUB-CONTRACTORS ARE INCLUDED

1939
1,115,060   412,880
109,200
TOTAL 1,636,940 SQ. FT.
TWICE 1935
PERSONNEL 12,500

MAIN FACTORIES | DISPERSAL EVACUATION PREMISES
DERBY
CREWE
GLASGOW
NORTHERN FACTORIES & NEWCASTLE UNDER LYME

1941
1,235,910   682,030   742,050   1,833,000   159,420
150,000
TOTAL 4,804,410 SQ. FT.   6 TIMES 1935
PERSONNEL 38,600

1943
1,516,040   1,062,930   522,300   965,400   2,153,500   203,600
178,000
TOTAL 6,601,770 SQ. FT.   8·2 TIMES 1935
PERSONNEL 55,640

1944
1,621,790   1,236,560   329,200   1,107,700   2,211,500   101,500
400,000   220,270
TOTAL 7,228,520 SQ. FT.   9 TIMES 1935
PERSONNEL 57,067

31. The explosive expansion of the Rolls-Royce production facilities between 1935 and 1944. Hives spent the whole of the war travelling from factory to factory and also visiting London, at times weekly, to attend meetings of the War Cabinet.

32. A Merlin-powered Lancaster of RAF Bomber Command flying towards Hitler's Berchtesgaden Chalet.

improved rate of climb and an increase of some 40 mph in top speed at 25,000 feet and above. This estimate, together with the fact that her tank capacity would give her longer range, meant that the Mustang, when fitted with the Merlin, would be superior to any other fighter at that time.

Harker experienced difficulties in persuading the powers-that-be, but with the support of Ray Dorey he eventually convinced Hives. According to Harker, Hives said: 'If you really believe that it will do as you say and be superior to the Focke-Wulf 190, then we must do it.'

Hives telephoned Sir Wilfrid Freeman and discussions began between Rolls-Royce and the Air Ministry. The drawback to installing the new Merlin 61 (which had been Harker's recommendation) was the fact that the Ministry wanted every Merlin 61 available to go into Spitfires to counter the new Fw 190.

To an extent, Rolls-Royce were in sympathy with this view, as is made clear in this memo from his assistant, Bill Lappin, to Hives on 14 May 1942, after a meeting at the Ministry:

Re: Mustang

At a meeting yesterday on a very high level, it was suggested to the Minister that the LX1 should be tried in the above machine, so you may hear about this, but if not you could put it on your list of points for next meeting with CDR.

I feel myself that it might pay a very good dividend, if it can be done quickly, to install the Merlin XX in this machine.

Discussions ranged back and forth, but soon tests took place, both at Hucknall and in the USA. In the USA, the proponents of installing the Merlin 61 into the Mustang found an important ally in Major Thomas (Tommy) Hitchcock, a former fighter ace of the First World War who became Assistant Air Attaché at the American Embassy in London. At the end of 1942, he gave a briefing to the Assistant Chief of Staff for Intelligence in Washington, saying, *inter alia*:

This fighter business in Europe is a little bit like the women's dress business ... the question of styles and fashions keeps changing all the time. When I went back to London about seven months ago, the English Fighter Command wouldn't look at anything that wouldn't fly at 28,000 to 30,000 feet and have plenty of speed. Since then the Focke Wulf has come into active participation on the Western Front; and now all the talk you hear is about greater climb and additional acceleration. This is because the Focke Wulf had those capabilities to a very great degree.

The whole story of the English fighter planes is more a story of engines than it is of the planes themselves. When you talk about engines, you get practically down to the Rolls engine – that is the Rolls Merlin engine. It started out at about 850 hp with a critical altitude of around 15,000 feet.

Now, when I first went over there, I was rather surprised to run into a report that the Mustang, which is our P-51, was 35 miles an hour faster than the Spitfire V at around 15,000 feet. At 25,000 feet it went a few miles an hour faster and was pulling 290 less hp. That indicated there must be something aerodynamically good about the Mustang. Dr. E.P. Warner, prominent aeronautical engineer in this country, came over to England and made considerable studies as to the aerodynamic quality of the fighter planes. He reduced it to co-efficient drag. The Mustang had a very low co-efficient drag as compared to the Spitfire and that is why it goes faster. It had the lowest co-efficient of drag of any plane in that theatre; and the English gave it a very good report and became very enthusiastic about it.

They said, 'Now, if we can put a high altitude engine in this plane we will have the answer to a maiden's prayer.' So they put a Merlin 61 engine in it; and they have got us to put one into it in this country. Originally they were going to put in the 61 that peaked at 30,000 feet. Then because the Focke Wulf peaks at 21,000 feet (and because the Spitfire is lighter than the Mustang) they decided the thing to do was to let the Spitfires have the high cover, and try and make the Mustang a fighter against the Focke Wulf. They took the Merlin 61 engine and put a different blower ratio on it so as to get the critical altitude at 21,000 feet, and this is the plane which gives about 426 miles an hour at 21,000 feet. Their original thought was to bring it up higher with the 61 version that peaked at 30,000 feet.

The white hope of the English, in order to combat the Fw-190, and particularly the Focke Wulf with the fully rated engine (which they are probably up against now), is by putting the Merlin 61 into the Mustang. They believe that will be the best fighting plane for the next year or two; and their preliminary tests indicate they are right.

Mark Arnold-Foster wrote in *The World at War*:

If they were to bomb by day over Europe, what the Americans needed was a long-range fighter. They had reached the same point of frustration that the Luftwaffe had reached at the end of the Battle of Britain. The bombers. The Allies, unlike the Germans, found a solution. It was the North American P-51B Mustang fighter, powered by the Rolls-Royce engine. The Mustang was probably the most remarkable combat aeroplane produced during World War Two. It represented the ultimate development of the highly stressed internal combustion piston-engined aeroplane.

The Mustang with the Merlin outperformed, as Harker had promised Hives it would, both the Messerschmitt 109 and the Focke-Wulf 190. In a memo to Sir Wilfrid Freeman on 8 November 1942, Hives wrote:

The results in the air fitted with the Merlin engine confirm that with the same power the Mustang is 20/25 mph faster than the Spitfire. We appreciated the inherent qualities as soon as one of our test pilots flew one at Duxford in May last, and realised its possibilities.

We do not look upon the Mustang as a replacement Spitfire, we look upon it as a replacement Hurricane … We can anticipate that Fighter Command might choose the Mustang in preference to the Spitfire unless something is done to overcome the obvious faults which we have mentioned (poor quality manufacture and finish).

Eventually, more than 12,000 Merlins were built for the Mustang.

After the US Eighth Air Force lost a number of bombers on a disastrous raid on Schweinfurt, it ordered substantial numbers of the Merlin-powered P-51B Mustang. In *A Short History of Air Power*, James Stokesbury wrote:

Deliverance of another sort was at hand, however, in the appearance of the North American P-51 Mustang, a happy marriage of an American airframe designed for a British purchasing mission and the great Merlin engine. The Mustang's conception went all the way back to 1940, but the first American combat group to fly them did not get to Britain until November 1943, which gives some idea of the lead time necessary to create the whole air-force system. On December 1, Mustangs flew their first long-range escort mission, nearly 500 miles to Kiel and back. That was just the beginning. By March 1944, the Mustangs, the bombers' 'little friends', escorted Flying Fortresses and Liberators all the way to Berlin, 1,100 miles. No longer were German fighters free to make their killing passes at the hard-pressed formations of plodding heavy bombers. Allied fighters over Berlin meant air supremacy, fulfilling Trenchard's old dictum that command of the air begins at the enemy's aerodromes. The few Germans knowledgeable about air war knew they had lost when they saw Mustangs over the heart of the Reich. The corner was turned at last.

This was the verdict of Sholto Douglas:

The Mustang after it had been built with our Merlin engines which were built under licence in the United States, became one of the finest and most versatile of all the fighters that were produced during the Second World War.

TILLY SCHILLING

The Merlin engine justifiably achieved an enviable reputation but, as with all mechanical devices, it suffered its share of problems. There were very few on single-engine installations (see page 35 for cylinder block problems) or on the Lancaster whose powerplants were carried well forward of the wing. The biggest problems arose on the Halifax and Mosquito. The Halifax suffered no fewer than 95 gear reduction failures in a period of six months. The powerplant was set close to the wing and well above the leading edge, causing a great deal of disturbed airflow around the propellers. The three-blade propellers meant considerable vibration for the engine, and a change to four-blade propellers was tried. It brought some improvement.

Ronnie Harker, in his liaison role, heard of any complaints from the front line. He recalled that, during the Battle of Britain and for some time after, there were a number of big-end failures. Sometimes these caused a fire, leading to a forced landing or even the abandoning of the aircraft. Cyril Lovesey, in charge of engine development, tried everything he knew on the test beds, but could not establish the cause. Harker tried in the air with a flight that included 167 slow rolls and twelve vertical dives, but still could not replicate the failure. The problem was finally solved by a Wing Commander Boyd at the Aircraft and Armament Evaluation Establishment at Boscombe Down. He took an aircraft up to 30,000 feet, rolled it on its back, thus losing oil pressure, over-revved to 3,600 rpm and, with a slight negative 'G' force all the way down, held this condition. This meant that the engine was exceeding maximum rpm for at least 30 seconds while starved of oil, and therefore air was getting to the bearings instead of oil.

Hives took a very close interest in any complaints coming back from both the test pilots and those in combat action. Perhaps the most intractable problem they faced was what became known as the 'skewgear failure'. Alex Henshaw describes it in detail in his book *Sigh for a Merlin*. Suffice it here to say that there were several failures, and as Henshaw put it:

These skewgear failures were more disturbing because there was no warning of any kind and they often occurred after a machine had been climbed, dived at full throttle, tested and probably had several landings and adjustments.

Finally, on 18 July 1942, Henshaw suffered a nearly fatal crash in the Black Country, virtually demolishing a house. As a result, tremendous pressure was brought to bear from Hives to find the cause of the trouble. Alec Harvey-Bailey, with his father in charge of defect investigation on the Merlin and Griffon during the war, remembered that both engine testing and failure investigation were treated with great respect:

At the start of a new factory or new engine type, all engines were endurance tested, stripped and rebuilt for final test. As engine conditions permitted this was eased until only a sample of engines were stripped, the remainder being endurance final tested and, if satisfactory, despatched. This system was no formality. One would find very senior people on the inspection lines seeing for themselves. At that time a number of features, such as reduction gear tip correction and tooth alignment, was determined almost entirely by bedding patterns. Bearings, pistons and rings, and joint conditions would be looked at critically and, if warnings were present of impending trouble, action would be initiated. Later in the War, Production Proof Tests were introduced when sample engines from the line would be subjected to the last 25 hours of the type test and then examined with the object of seeing troubles that might not show on normal non-easement engines. If one reads this in context with the failure investigation activity and the monitoring of repair engine condition, and recognising the short timescales involved, it will be seen that there was an effective system for handling the situation.

As Derby built pilot quantities of major new types, various parameters including final performance limits and such things as piston profiles, ring gaps and other features would be established on production, not without some lively and competitive arguments with other interested parties.

To help Alec Harvey-Bailey further, Rolls-Royce's liaison pilots, such as Ronnie Harker and Athol McIntyre, visited squadrons and brought home broken bits in their Spitfires and Mustangs. And indeed it was Alec's father, R.W.H. Bailey, whom Hives put in charge of the skewgear failure inquiry. When the problem was finally solved, Alex Henshaw remembers that Hives telephoned him personally to say that the solution had been found.

By January 1941, with the Battle of Britain won, the RAF began sorties over Northern France, and complaints started to come back from the Spitfire pilots (because of their greater speed, Spitfires were used rather than Hurricanes) that the improved Me 109F and the Focke-Wulf 190 were outperforming the Spitfire. Sholto Douglas wrote later:

In the introduction of new aircraft with improved performance it was still, as always, a see-saw, with first one side and then the other gaining the upper hand. With our improved Spitfires we had caught up with the Me 109F. The struggle had remained on a fairly equal footing until towards the latter part of the summer of 1941; and then we were caught flat-footed. My pilots reported seeing over Amiens a new type of radial-engined fighter. It was in the course of one of the Circus operations, and there were some particularly experienced pilots flying in the wings from Kenley, Tangmere and Northolt. Our intelligence people ridiculed the idea. But what the pilots reported was correct: they were seeing for the first time the Focke-Wulf 190.

We have already seen how problems arose on the Halifax and this is what Alec Harvey-Bailey wrote about those and other problems in his *The Merlin in Perspective – The Combat Years*:

The Mosquito problem arose from the proximity of the propeller tips to the fuselage producing a first propeller order vibration causing reduction gear troubles. A great deal of design effort went into the engines for both aircraft types to make the reduction gears work reliably under the imposed loadings and this is discussed later in the text. The Mosquito problem would however respond to using increased rpm and it became practice to operate at 2400 rpm or above when operations permitted.

Engines in these aircraft tended to suffer failures of the joint washers between the main structural joints. This was cured by deleting the washers on all engines and using the Alan Squires SQ jointing compounds. Alan was one of the characters of the Company and I regarded him as a mechanical chemist for his work on jointing compounds and cooling systems, all conducted from a tiny laboratory behind the technical block at Nightingale Road.

One other problem with the early Merlins was the limitation imposed by the float-type carburettors. A rapid dive would cause the engine to cut because the float chamber was drained. The Messerschmitt 109E did not suffer the same problem, as its Daimler-Benz 601A engine did not have a carburettor – it used a direct-injection fuel system instead. The German pilots soon appreciated the opportunity, and could escape Hurricanes and Spitfires on their tail by going into a steep dive. If they attempted to follow, the British aircraft would splutter and misfire, the propeller would go into fine pitch, which slowed the dive even more, and when the engine picked up again it would overspeed violently. Even if the British rolled into the dive, they still lost ground.

The problem was partially solved by an ingenious engineer at the RAE at Farnborough, Miss Tilly Schilling. She developed a washer with a small calibrated hole to place in the fuel supply line, the small hole passing just enough fuel for full power at sea level under negative 'G' conditions. Pilots, perhaps better known for straightforwardness than subtlety, referred to the device as 'Miss Schilling's orifice', and it was installed throughout Fighter Command by March 1941.

Gordon Dawson, who worked under Harry Cantrill in the Testing Department (largely on developing the Griffon engine), remembered that it was learnt pretty quickly after the Schilling solution that the Americans had found a complete cure for the problem with the Bendix pressure diaphragm carburettor, but it took some time to secure supplies. In the meantime, both Rolls-Royce and the SU carburettor company, in conjunction with the RAE at Farnborough, developed anti-'G' versions of the Merlin carburettor. Both worked well, but were replaced by the Bendix carburettor when it became available.

As we have seen, there were many elements contributing to the success of the Merlin and one that should not be forgotten was the contribution made by Rolls-Royce's testing facilities at Hucknall.

The Rolls-Royce aero engine had been a logical progression from the Silver Ghost car, but whereas the company manufactured chassis and, ultimately, complete cars, it never became an aircraft manufacturer. Others, such as Armstrong Siddeley, Bristol and de Havilland, made both aircraft and aero engines.

There was a big advantage to Rolls-Royce's approach – it could sell to all aircraft manufacturers without worrying that priority be given to its own aircraft. There was also a big disadvantage – there were problems in installing the engines, so that the aircraft customers often had to be shown how to do it. This disadvantage became very apparent with the Eagle and the Falcon, on which the aircraft manufacturers made a poor job of the 'plumbing' (the radiator, piping and so on).

Rolls-Royce came to realise that they had to do more than supply an engine, a handbook and a starting handle. Cyril Lovesey, a private pilot with his own aeroplane, saw the need very clearly. Early attempts to establish a testing operation were hampered by the need to put all resources into developing the 'R' engine for the Schneider Trophy. There was also talk of a national plan to develop a 'centre for speed' somewhere in East Anglia. However, the plan died in the cold blast of the Depression. Nevertheless, some testing was carried out on behalf of Rolls-Royce by the Nottingham Flying Club in the early 1930s.

By the mid-1930s it was clear that the company would have to establish its own facilities. Lovesey took the lead and set up an operation at Hucknall in Nottinghamshire, alongside the RAF. Initially, there was just a hangar to maintain the aircraft, an engineering team (especially skilled on fabrications) and ground test facilities. Lovesey brought the young engineer Ray Dorey over from Derby, and put him in charge of the staff of 25.

Captain Ronnie Shepherd, who had already carried out some testing for the company at the Nottingham Flying Club, was appointed chief test pilot. Their first complement of aircraft in one hangar consisted of a Hawker Hart, a Hawker Fury and a Gloster Gnatsnapper. It was at Hucknall on 12 April 1935 that the PV12 engine flew for the first time, in a Hawker Hart biplane. Most of its first 60 hours in the air were spent on perfecting the cooling system.

Hucknall expanded rapidly during the war, undertaking a

great deal of installation work as well as a greatly increased test-flying programme. For example, the Merlin powerplant for the Lancaster bomber was designed and built at Hucknall, as were the prototype installations for the Griffon, Beaufighter and Henley. During the Battle of Britain, a Hurricane repair line was set up.

Ray Dorey organised the Hucknall operation so efficiently that its repair of Hurricane fighters contributed vitally to the number of aircraft capable of flying in the desperate months of August and September 1940. And it was at Hucknall that the Merlin 65 was installed in a Mustang and flown within three months. (North American Aviation, who were also carrying out the conversion, took much longer to complete the operation.) At the same time, in 1942, Hucknall contributed to converting Spitfire Vs to Spitfire IXs, to counter the German Fw 190.

Also stationed at Hucknall was Rolls-Royce's RAF liaison team, which flew regularly to the RAF stations on which Rolls-Royce engines operated, and whose job it was to maintain close contact with the RAF and report to Hives, who listened to them very carefully. Many of the liaison team were Rolls-Royce employees who had flown in the RAFVR or RAuxAF before the war. Some had flown in the Battle of Britain. Alec Harvey-Bailey had reason to be grateful to the liaison team. As he said in *The Merlin in Perspective – The Combat Years*, written for the Rolls-Royce Heritage Trust:

The Liaison Pilots were helpful in our failure investigation work, particularly when we were in real difficulty, maintaining a two way traffic of communication separate from formal channels. As an example, at the height of the Halifax reduction gear problems Ronnie Harker was able to fly me to 4 Group headquarters at York and to visit some of the worst affected stations including Elvington, Breighton, Rufforth and Holme-on-Spalding Moor in the course of one Saturday. This enabled me to brief the Senior Air Staff Officer, the Group Engineering Officer, station officers and squadron pilots. Aided by Ronnie I was able to put over the problems and the action being taken, and re-establish confidence which had been on the wane. It also enabled us to get Group to press from its end for four-bladed propellers which were a quick alleviation to the problems.

QUILL LIKED THE GRIFFON

The first reference to the engine which became the Griffon was in a memo from Royce dated 22 August 1930, in which he requested that an 'H' (Buzzard) engine be built with a double helical reduction gear, which would give quieter running. This engine became known as the Modified 'H' engine. There was little progress during 1931, because of the concentration on the Schneider Trophy. The first time the Griffon name was applied was on a design scheme, DES 1618, dated 30 January 1932. The first run of Griffon Serial No. 1 was on 6 January 1933, and the last run of this engine was in 1934. The programme was abandoned in the spring of 1936 as priority was given to the Merlin. Initially, the Merlin also had double helical reduction gears, but when it suffered failures it moved on to straight spur gears, as did the Griffon.

At the beginning of 1939 Hives, already appreciating the need for a more powerful Merlin, ordered the development of a new Griffon to be interchangeable with the Merlin; thereafter the Griffon of the early 1930s was referred to as the 'old' Griffon. The new Griffon was called Griffon I, and ran for the first time on 30 November 1939. However, it was clear by then that it was too heavy, and a weight-saving project was put in hand. Harry Cantrill, who had joined Rolls-Royce from Armstrong Siddeley, and his team took 200 lb off the weight of the engine. This lighter engine became the Griffon II (the Griffon I, of which only three were built, was abandoned). The Griffon II first ran on 26 June 1940, but suffered a number of problems, including torsional vibration of the crankshaft. This was corrected by changing the firing order and by altering the mounting system from back and middle to back and front. This modified Griffon was called the Griffon IIB, and first ran in December 1940.

The Griffon IIB performed well from the start, undergoing its type test and going into production with remarkably little further development. An intensive programme then started for more power and higher rated altitude, with a range of different specifications to suit various applications. The latter was simplified by the new auxiliary gearbox carrying many of the accessories which in the case of the Merlin had been engine-mounted. This avoided the need for many engine modifications. The first actual engine modification, implemented shortly after production started, was the switch to the Bendix injection carburettor to cure the negative 'G' problem (before the Merlin).

Following the experience with the Merlin, a two-stage supercharged version came quickly, and in two years boost went up from plus 12 lb per square inch to plus 25 lb per square inch, power from 1,700 hp to 2,300 hp, and FS rated altitude from 14,500 feet to 26,000 feet. Meanwhile, development was proceeding, and the major decision here was to continue with the forward cam and magneto drives but to revert to rear crank drive for the supercharger. Important innovations were the end oil-feed crankshaft (which made the main and big-end bearings much less vulnerable) and an external drive for a gearbox which carried all the auxiliaries and freed the engine from the multiple drives for these. It also had an improved supercharger and an updraught carburettor with a number of other detailed improvements. As the higher grades of fuel became available in service, the engine was able to use the boost they permitted. The addition of water-methanol injection on top of the plus 25 lb boost gave a take-off rating of about 2,500 hp. The heavy programme went through with a few problems, which were solved, and the engine was very successful in service.

By late 1939, both the Air Ministry and Supermarine were showing interest in the possibility of the Griffon being installed in the Spitfire. Sir Wilfrid Freeman's interest was significant, because earlier in 1939 he had been discussing the idea of turning Supermarine over to production of the Beaufighter. Opinion at Supermarine itself was that every possible power increase should be squeezed from the Merlin, but that eventually it would be superseded by the Griffon. At Derby, Hives was heard to refer to it as 'the second power string for the Spitfire'. Joe Smith at Supermarine said, 'A good big 'un will always beat a good little 'un', and he wanted the Griffon tested in a Spitfire as soon as possible.

During the summer and autumn of 1940, other more pressing events delayed any testing of the Griffon, and it was not until 27 November 1941 that Jeffrey Quill made a test flight in a Mark III airframe fitted with a Griffon engine, the RG 2SM. This aircraft was designated the Mark IV. This is what Quill wrote about it later:

The main differences, insofar as they affected the pilot, were: because the Griffon engine rotated the opposite way to the Merlin, it caused the aeroplane to swing right-handed instead of left-handed on the take-off; there was somewhat less ground clearance, resulting in a slight reduction in propeller diameter; the power available for take-off was much greater; and the engine RPM were lower than in the Merlin.

All this meant that the throttle needed to be handled judiciously on take-off but, once in the air, the aeroplane had a great feeling of power about it; it seemed the airborne equivalent of a very powerful sports car and was great fun to fly. Changes of trim with changes of power were much more in evidence, both directionally and longitudinally, and the aeroplane sheared about a bit during tight manoeuvres and simulated dog-fights. I realised at once that we should have to correct its directional characteristics and probably its longitudinal stability also, both of which, in due time, we achieved. Indeed, DP845 eventually went through many phases of development, remaining in our flight development unit throughout, and I, and others, flew in it a great deal; it became one of our favourite aeroplanes.

However, by the end of 1941, the two-stage supercharger with intercooler system was being fitted to the Merlin, and the single-stage Griffon had been leapfrogged. As a result, the Mark IV had no production future, but the practicality of fitting a Griffon into a Spitfire had been proved. There was every reason to think that whatever supercharger technology was applied to the Merlin could also be applied to the Griffon.

Further developments to build a new Spitfire with a big two-stage Griffon were put in hand, but in the meantime Jeffrey Quill showed what could be done in a Spitfire with a single-stage Griffon – 'by then almost my favourite aircraft with its spectacular rate of climb "off the deck" and very good low-level performance', as he put it. In July 1942, Quill was asked to race this Spitfire against an Fw 190 and a Typhoon in front of some VIPs at Farnborough. He wrote about the day later:

On reflection the general scheme became clear. The Spitfire was to be a sort of datum pacemaker – 'Mr Average Contemporary Fighter' – and its job would be to come in last, the real excitement of the proceedings being by how much it would be beaten by the Fw 190 and the Typhoon, and which of these two bright stars would beat the other and by how much. Outside on the tarmac at Worthy Down stood the inoffensive-looking but highly potent DP845. Nobody had said what sort of Spitfire I should bring. Just a Spitfire. I rang up Joe Smith. 'Joe', I said, 'about this thing at Farnborough. I reckon if I take DP845 I will beat the pair of them. Will that upset any applecarts?' 'You bet it will', he said. 'Take it.'

At Farnborough I parked DP845 as inconspicuously as I could and walked into Willy Wilson's office. Kenneth Seth-Smith of Hawkers had arrived with his Typhoon, and we discussed the plan.

We would all three take off together and fly to a point westwards of the aerodrome at Odiham. We would then head back towards Farnborough in open line abreast at a moderate cruising speed at 1,000 ft, Willy Wilson in the centre with the Fw 190 and Seth-Smith and myself on each side. At a signal from Willy we would all open up simultaneously to full power and head for the finishing line at Farnborough where the assembled VIPs would be waiting.

All went according to plan until, when we were about half-way between Odiham and Farnborough and going flat out, I was beginning to overhaul Fw 190 and Typhoon. Suddenly I saw sparks and black smoke coming from the Fw 190's exhaust and at that moment Willy also saw it and throttled back his BMW engine and I shot past him and never saw him again. I was also easily leaving the

Typhoon behind and the eventual finishing order was, first the Spitfire, second the Typhoon, third the Fw 190.

This was precisely the opposite result to that expected or indeed intended. It certainly put the cat among the pigeons, and among the VIPs. When I taxied in, everybody crowded round the DP845, as the message sank in that it was the Griffon Spitfire which had handsomely beaten what were then supposed to be the two fastest fighters in service. The sensation was considerable.

Although the engine ended with a long list of Mark numbers, there were only five production applications – Firefly, Spitfire, Seafire, Barracuda and Shackleton – and only the first two of these initially. There was in addition a considerable range of prototypes: Beaufighter, Hawker Henley, Tempest and Fury, Seagull, Martin Baker MB5, Blackburn B54, Spiteful and Seafang. Although useful as prototype testbeds, these were replaced in service by gas-turbine-engined aircraft.

The Griffon 100/120 series was the ultimate version intended for the Spitfire 21, Spiteful, Seafire 46 and Seafang, most of which were prototypes. All of these had three-speed, two-stage superchargers, and some had contra-rotating propellers.

As the war progressed, the two-stage took over from the single-stage Griffon and led the development effort. The last Griffons to be produced were the 37 for the Barracuda and, after further improvements, the 57 and 58 for the Avro Shackleton. The Griffon 58 was cleared originally in 1946 for the Shackleton prototype, but stayed in production until 1955; one was redelivered to the RAF, after a major overhaul at the Glasgow factory, as late as 1986.

The Griffon remained in service in the Shackleton until 1991, operating on a daily basis at nearly 2,500 hp at take-off and with a life of 2,000 hours. This was the same power achieved in 1931 by its forebear, the 'R' engine, with the same bore and stroke but with a life of only one hour, a fine example of the progress of detailed mechanical development over a period of 60 years.

There are those who believe that it was the Griffon that

ultimately made the Spitfire the outstanding fighter of the war. And it was not just performance that endeared it to the RAF. The service personnel reported that it had the best test record of any engine they handled, with a higher percentage of Griffons reaching their overhaul time limit without mechanical problems than any other type of engine.

CHAPTER EIGHT

HARD POUNDING

'A COMPLETE MESS'
A THOUSAND MILES INTO RUSSIA
'THEY WILL LISTEN TO MY APPEAL'
THE MOST INTENSE INDUSTRIAL EFFORT

'A COMPLETE MESS'

Though Hives was in general agreement with the policy of developing new and, everyone hoped, more powerful engines he refused to allow the development of the Griffon to interfere with that of the two-stage Merlin, on which work had started early in 1940. This again was to prove a far-sighted decision. The firm stand which Hives took on the subject of developing existing engines was amply vindicated by the events of 1942 and 1943.

The last six months of 1941 saw a steady, if inadequate, rise in the output of the whole group. Both Derby and Crewe were at peak load, Glasgow was approaching full production and the output of complete engines from the Ford works in Manchester had started in August. The total production from all four factories in 1941 amounted to 12,227 engines, of which 7,517 were produced in the last six months of the year. The majority of these, towards the latter part of the year, were Merlin XXs which were intended to engine the Lancaster and Halifax and for the production of which both the mass-production factories (Glasgow and Fords) had been tooled up.

The production record of the firm had nevertheless come in for heavy criticism during the year. In July 1941 the Deputy Director of Engine Production at the MAP, Mr Pate, wrote a report in which he severely criticised the performance of the group. He considered that the programme was in 'a complete mess' because of 'wholesale changes of type' and that the firm had shown 'the most lamentable lack of real planning ability and foresight'. Rolls-Royce, in view of the resources which had been 'made available' to them, had, in his opinion, the worst record of the engine firms, and he concluded that it had 'outworn the managerial capacity of its highest control'. Mr Pate was far more concerned with the fact that the firm had not fulfilled its programmes than with its actual achievement in terms of production and development. But his criticism will not stand the test of analysis, for though from time to time the firm had virtually created a desperate shortage by producing at short notice an engine which was urgently required to increase performance in some direction or another, the total output of engines of all types was still greatly in excess of the absorption into the new aircraft. Hives was well aware that he would incur criticism as a result of pursuing a strong independent policy but by this time he was convinced of its soundness.

As he pointed out to the board early in 1941, if it had not been for his rigid adherence to the policy of Merlin development the only fighter machines that would have been available would have had a performance greatly inferior to that of the latest German aircraft. 'The Board should be aware that in pursuing this policy we have certainly upset some of the M.A.P. officials, but on the other hand we have added to our goodwill with the R.A.F. We had contracts to cover us to produce the old type engines and as far as we were concerned it would obviously have been a very much easier manufacturing problem.' Mr Pate's criticism was obviously based on a rigid quantitative approach which ignored several of the most important factors.

One of the remedies for this state of affairs was considered to be an increase in the direct control exercised over the management. It was also considered that more effective and accurate programming would have a beneficial effect on output. But more effective programming required more complete information and both the attempt to obtain information and the attempt to apply the results of any analysis which it made possible were inclined to cause friction which at times could become serious. Ministry officials were inclined to issue requests for information without considering the effort which the provision of this information required. On 30 October Sir Alexander Dunbar wrote to Hives saying that although, as he knew, Rolls-Royce looked upon controls as a nuisance, the Light Alloy Control were unable to function effectively for lack of information on Rolls-Royce stocks. S.H. Grylls, who had to deal with requests of this kind, pointed out that this would involve a week's work for the whole equipment staff and asked that the firm should be exempted from this request. 'If it is to be a precedent for similar communications', he said, 'we just have not got the staff to deal with it.' Shortly afterwards Hives himself replied that the management would do what it could to provide the information. 'I have every sympathy with controls', he added, 'and with my modest responsibility of trying to look after three factories I have acquired a very clear picture of why the League of Nations failed.'

It was deliberate MAP and Air Ministry policy to interfere with the Rolls-Royce group as little as was consistent with the minimum of centralised control which the Ministries felt obliged to attempt to exercise over production as a whole. The firm's technical record was so outstanding and the dependence of the RAF on Rolls-Royce engines so great that even though those in authority thought that the production record might be improved by more direct control no one was prepared to carry the responsibility for any failure which such interference might have caused. The graph which recorded the horsepower per pound of the Merlin was the thin red line of the Second World War. The management also made it quite clear that it did not regard the existing apparatus of control as being very constructive. 'We are concerned', Hives remarked in a letter to Sir Charles Craven in April 1941, 'by the number of additional officials we are getting from Government departments. We have an overseer and assistant, an R.T.O. and assistants, the A.I.D. and assistants, an M.A.P. representative and assistants. They are either sensible and acknowledge they know nothing about the problem and do nothing, or they irritate us by attempting to query decisions which they cannot possibly understand.'

The so-called production failures were in any case failures in a relative sense only – by comparison with the firm's own promises or with the even more extravagant expectations of the programmes. The latter were inevitably compromises, stretched between the irreducible minima of strategic require-ments and the depressing maxima which a realistic appreciation of the possibilities always provided. Reasons for them could always be found and in 1941 these were not lacking. In February Hives told the board that the output of the group had definitely suffered as a result of the raids on Coventry, Birmingham and Sheffield. Crewe itself was bombed by a lone raider in the same month, resulting in both damage and casualties. This resulted in a request from the employees for additional protection. In addition as the year progressed various shortages – machine tools, labour and components (particularly carburettors) – began to occupy more and more of the management's attention. Very little could be done about machine tools.

In December 1940 S.E. Blackstone had calculated that the increased output demanded from the group would require 1,175 new machine tools, assuming no change in the propor-tion of work sub-contracted. This figure was calculated on the basis of tools required to increase production from 177 to 300 Merlins a week assuming a 65 per cent utilisation of machines working 130 hours a week on the two-shift system. Only 423 tools had been asked for and consequently the increased output could be obtained only by improving the machine load balancing (i.e. ensuring that the output of a line of machines was not held up by a 'bottleneck' machine), by reducing the machine hours per operation by improved methods or transferring operations from machines where these could be performed by fitters, or by increasing sub-contracting. Neither Derby nor Crewe kept accurate machine loading records at this time and consequently any general planning for the whole group was made imprecise and difficult. Blackstone considered that a reduction of machining hours from 1,630 to 1,250 was the most that could be hoped for under the circumstances. Statistical comparisons made between the two factories in June 1941 illustrate the effect on efficiency of different production techniques and layouts. Derby machining hours were 53 per cent higher than Glasgow while Crewe machining hours were only 11 per cent higher.

The limiting factor in the expansion of the Glasgow and Ford factories in particular was gear-cutting machine tools. Until July 1941 gears were produced by the batch system and on Blackstone's recommendation (which could not be carried out when it was first made because of the danger of dislocating production early in 1941) the machines were reorganised on a line system. This resulted in a remarkable improvement from 35 to 70 engine sets per week, but the programmes issued late in 1941 required an even greater increase in output. The charts from which the production build-up was controlled were the machine tool delivery charts, and throughout 1941 and 1942 gear-cutting machine tools remained the limiting factor.

A THOUSAND MILES INTO RUSSIA

The Directorate of Engine Production at the MAP was nevertheless critical of the achievement at Glasgow, an achievement which was much more accurately recorded statistically than that of any of the other factories. It was suggested, with some justification, that the elaboration of the reports was in inverse ratio to the output of engines. It was ironical nevertheless that the Directorate, which had a vested interest in statistics, should suggest that engines and not statistics were needed to defeat the enemy. The management would have been the first to agree that this was so but the Directorate would not readily have relinquished its right to extend the statistical stethoscope into every corner of the industrial system.

The statistics were in fact deceptive if the judgement of the Glasgow record was to be based on the output of engines only. A large volume of parts had been supplied to the other factories and for use as spares and the conversion of this output into equivalent engines revealed a production achievement which was not unimpressive. Hives challenged the Directorate to quote a better production record than Glasgow and they were unable to do so. The Glasgow output, as he was quick to point out, was achieved despite considerable interference from Ministry officials of various kinds. At times this interference had serious repercussions and on one occasion he found it necessary to give orders that under no circumstances was a certain senior official to be admitted to the Hillington factory. 'All we want to do', he wrote to Air Commodore Weedon, the Director of Repairs and Maintenance, 'is to get on with the job. If somebody is going to tell us how many spanners we require, how many stands we require, and how many cleaning tanks we require, then I think it is time Rolls-Royce were relieved of any additional repairs. If you look at the map you will find that Hitler has penetrated 1,000 miles into Russia up to the present while we have been waiting for the M.A.P. to make up their minds on Vulture repairs.'

Rolls-Royce naturally received a high priority for labour but the shortage of skilled men, particularly of those able to hold responsible administrative positions, began to reach serious proportions in 1941. This question came up repeatedly at the Ford works in Manchester. This was the only factory making complete Merlins in England which was not managed by Rolls-Royce. Ford engineers had spent several months at Derby and maintained a close liaison, but like so many others the planning staff at Fords had underestimated the skilled labour requirements and were in consequence facing many unexpected problems in building up output. This was in no way a direct responsibility of Rolls-Royce but the Directorate of Engine Production considered that an all-round increase in production might be obtained by forming a single pool for skilled labour for all four Merlin factories. This proposal, which was put up to Hives by Major Bulman, would clearly have involved a severe drain on the skilled labour at Derby and Crewe, which had already been heavily drawn upon to help Glasgow, for the benefit of Fords. This would have restricted output of the more recent and difficult marks of Merlin, which were always in high demand, and whose production inevitably required a much higher degree of skill in the initial stages. 'We shall leave you', suggested Major Bulman, 'to explore the situation by yourselves without external interference or influence, realising, however, that when you have mutually agreed as to what transfers are feasible the Ministry of Labour will be asked to exert any pressure necessary to get individuals to move.'

Hives would not countenance this proposal for a moment. He considered that the mere suggestion of such a scheme showed 'colossal impertinence' on the Directorate's part. 'You can take all the men you like away from Derby and Crewe', he replied, 'if they will go, but you also take the responsibility with them.' He considered that Fords were a much bigger organisation which were capable of looking after their own problems and that the danger of a skilled labour shortage had been quite obvious when he had visited the factory in the initial stages. The concern which this reply manifests arose partly from the fact that an excellent relationship had been established between Derby and the Manchester factory and Hives was afraid that the Ministry would upset this. He pointed out that Rolls-Royce had provided Fords with the parts for 60 complete engines to start their assembly line and he warned the Directorate that 'the day we stop providing them with pieces they will not be able to make another engine'.

'THEY WILL LISTEN TO MY APPEAL'

The Directorate's suggestion was of course made in good faith but it showed a failure to appreciate the relative importance of production at the different factories and the great danger which would be incurred by spreading the highly skilled technicians from Derby too thinly over the whole organisation. It also showed the somewhat theoretical approach of the administrator who, from repeated handling of the statistics of manpower, soon begins to consider that the human beings which the figures represent can be divided and multiplied and shifted from one factory or occupation to another as easily as the figures themselves. Though Major Bulman was not, as he later pointed out in reply, contemplating the transfer of more than 'a few men with actual Rolls-Royce experience' who he hoped would produce 'a snowball effect of rapid improvement', he did not realise the difficulties this involved. In a memorandum written on 7 September Hives replied at great length pointing out that he presumed Fords had been chosen because of their reserve of skilled labour at Dagenham.

On the labour position generally we came to an arrangement with the Ministry of Labour months ago that the Rolls-Royce group ... must be judged as a whole and not as independent units. On this question of transferring labour we have had considerable experience and the men just won't go. And if they are forced to go the rest of the factory just adopts a go-slow policy. Their attitude is that the Ministry of Labour and the M.A.P. go round to the factories that are doing well and keeping up with deliveries, and that as long as you are always behind hand with the output they will not take anybody away.

Many such realities of industrial administration had not been dreamt of in the philosophies of the central planners who sought to 'co-ordinate' the output of the Rolls-Royce group from Whitehall.

Hives turned next to the question of skilled labour. As he had once before had occasion to point out, the term 'skilled' no longer meant what it had meant in 1941. What had developed was simply a new version of the situation which was once neatly summarised by W.S. Gilbert in his immortal phrase 'when everyone is somebody then no one's anybody'. There were a number of men classed as skilled at Derby whom the management had no objection to transferring. 'But', Hives pointed out, 'they are of no use to Fords and no use to Glasgow.' The transfer problem for those who were of use was singularly acute. 'At the present time we have got the job of trying to persuade some people to go from Derby to Glasgow. The Ministry of Labour could not do it, but they will listen to my personal appeal.'

Such replies naturally did not satisfy the planners at MAP for they served only to accentuate their relative helplessness in the face of the infinite plasticity of human reactions even in the most closely controlled society. The intensity, direction and location of industrial effort cannot be cast into a rigid theoretical mould without severe losses, and the complexity of the social and industrial pattern is so great that any attempt to produce adjustments which are more than marginal in character will usually defeat the objective by altering the basic relationships between men and institutions in a manner which is quite unpredictable. Even the most marginal adjustments generate unforeseen difficulties and complexities.

The management had even less control of components, which were not, in many cases, the direct responsibility of Rolls-Royce, since the component firms supplied several engine manufacturers. From time to time severe shortages of certain components and accessories developed, sometimes as a result of bombing and sometimes as a result of the inability of the component manufacturers to expand production as fast as the engine factories. One of the most serious shortages in 1941 was carburettors. The S.U. Merlin carburettor was an intricate piece of mechanism which had never before (like so many other aero engine components) been manufactured in any quantity. Its production was also affected by bombing in 1941 and on 29 July no less than 620 engines were waiting for carburettors.

On 29 June, Hives contacted Mr Miles Thomas, Managing Director of the Nuffield group, and informed him that Rolls-Royce had already arranged to assist the S.U. Company by manufacturing bodies for Vulture, Peregrine, Griffon and Merlin carburettors and by making parts and jigs where necessary. He stressed that it was no use relying on Government departments to end the shortage and that only the Nuffield organisation itself could do this. On 17 July the position had become so serious that Hives offered to sacrifice engine production if necessary to help carburettor production. However, the steps taken earlier in June began to have effect and within a few weeks the output recovered sufficiently to clear the accumulated engines.

Powerplants were another item that presented supply difficulties towards the end of 1941. Rolls-Royce had undertaken considerable development work on these as a result of a decision made before the war that the powerplant should be the responsibility of the engine builder rather than the airframe manufacturer. Considerable numbers were built at Hucknall and at various sub-contractors throughout the country but the output from the sub-contractors was often not sufficient to clothe the engines. Though the output of powerplants from Rolls-Royce-controlled factories was substantial the majority were produced by independent sub-contractors and by the aircraft manufacturers themselves, and the supply difficulties were mainly in this area.

THE MOST INTENSE INDUSTRIAL EFFORT

Thus the years of crises completely fulfilled the predictions of the prophets even though the Blitzkrieg was not quite as devastating as they had imagined it would be. Industrial production showed a remarkable resilience in the face of bombing which was fortunately not as selective as it was intensive. Once secured by the victory of the summer and autumn of 1940 the supremacy of British air power required constant reinforcement by the most intense industrial effort. The strategic momentum and tactical initiative which this effort supplied depended almost entirely on a wise distribution of resources between production and development. The maximising of this effort depended in turn on a careful assessment of the trends of enemy aircraft design and the rate of development of existing enemy types, the unexploited potentialities of existing British engines and airframes, the comparative merit of new types, and the rate at which they could be safely introduced. This in its turn depended on the supply and flexibility of certain specialised factors of production such as machine tools and the most highly skilled labour.

The decision process was thus exceedingly complex, even though the ultimate objective was so clear and unequivocal. War may well simplify the economic problem but if the above must be considered a 'simple' situation its ramifications in time of peace should not be underrated. No hard and fast rules could be laid down but the apparatus of measurement and control was improved and by the end of 1941 the relationship between output and various variables by which resources were measured was more clearly ascertainable. It became possible in consequence to reduce the arbitrary element in the prediction of quantities and to assess the limits of expansion of the existing capacity. It was yet some time, however, before ministers and officials began to show an implicit understanding of the significance of the programme in its three-fold function as a psychological, a statistical and an administrative instrument. Even at the end of the war this tri-functional character had not been fully appreciated but in the following three years the general independence of these functions became much better understood. The MAP and the Air Ministry began to realise that though programmes would not perform miracles, miracles might on occasion be performed without programmes. The technique was an imperfect if essential method of illuminating and guiding the flow of industrial production. The trend towards 'realism' in the later years of the war is an indication of the fact that the Ministries found it both easier and more useful to adapt programmes to reality than reality to programmes.

Within this complex framework the policy of Rolls-Royce did not greatly change. The integrity and soundness of Hives's judgement and the tenacity with which he fought the case for Merlin development ensured that the RAF did not lack the right aircraft in 1941 or 1942 and earned him a considerable and well-deserved reputation. Despite criticism which was largely, if not always, ill-founded, he managed to maintain the full independence of the management during a most crucial period when many who were inevitably somewhat remote from reality, if not lacking in authority, must have been tempted by the urgency of the situation to interfere. On the whole the mutual confidence between the Directorates and the management was enhanced by the interchange of frank and forthright criticism which often reflected the passion of deeply held convictions and the concern of men who knew that a mistake could at best cost many lives and at worst lose the war. By comparison the last three years from 1942 to 1945 seem a period of calm in which a task was completed on the basis of foundations well and truly laid in the strenuous and exacting years which culminated in the Battle of Britain and its immediate aftermath.

The victory of the Battle of Britain and the proof which the events of 1941 provided that British industrial production was capable of withstanding the gradually diminishing power of the enemy's bombing offensive brought about a realisation that the Empire would have to plan for a war of attrition. Such a war could be won only by the most effective use of the resources at its command. During 1940 the immediate demands made by the intensity of the struggle made it necessary to waste in order to win. In 1941, though the struggle was no less intense, the war did not move spasmodically in favour of either side, and the administrative machine began, necessarily, to develop and to reassert itself. Current, rather than voltage, was now required to ensure victory. The elimination of the great uncertainties which existed in 1940 and 1941 made it possible for production to be both anticipated and directed more intelligently.

Late in 1941 the Cabinet decided to enlarge the heavy bomber programme with a view to attaining a front-line strength of 4,000 heavy bombers by July 1943. This figure required a production of 22,000 aircraft of which it was expected that 5,500 would be supplied from the United States. Such a figure necessarily involved a substantial increase in the output of engines, and in particular of engines from the Rolls-Royce group of factories. The Lancaster had shown early promise of being the most successful heavy bomber of the war and it was intended to be engined almost entirely by the Merlin. Several other aircraft were converted to Merlins when it was shown that this improved their performance, and several new aircraft were designed around Merlin or Griffon engines. The Rolls-Royce group alone obviously could not be expected to supply all the engines which this increased airframe output required and it was decided that a 20 per cent increase in the output of the group was the maximum which could be attained even under the most favourable conditions. The Packard Merlin production in the United States was beginning to build up and it was expected that 1,600 of these engines would be available in 1942 and a very much greater number in 1943 and 1944. Early in 1942 a further order for 14,000 Packard Merlins was placed with the Packard Company.

Hives did not doubt that this 20 per cent increase in the output of the Rolls-Royce group could be obtained provided that the necessary tools and labour were supplied. He estimated that it would require a total of 2,000 tools, spread over the Rolls-Royce factories alone (excluding Fords), and an increase of 10,000 in the labour force. He did not think that an increase in plant capacity was necessary, and in this he was strongly supported by Lord Beaverbrook, now Minister of Supply, who thought that a great deal of engine capacity was being wasted, particularly in the production of the Sabre. These estimates were accepted, and though it was realised that the provision of 2,000 machine tools for the Rolls-Royce group and a further 1,100 for the Ford factory would place a very great strain on the machine tool industry, arrangements for their supply were immediately made. The tools did not come forward as rapidly as was expected, but in due course all those originally promised were supplied.

A variety of estimates, all of which emerged in the form of programmes, were made of the increase in output which it was hoped these measures would provide. In February 1942, it was expected that the output of engines from the Rolls-Royce group (excluding Fords) would be 18,320 engines in 1942 and 22,860 in 1943. On 5 March this was revised downwards to 17,055 and 20,470 as a result of a clearer appreciation of some of the factors involved, particularly the rate of supply of machine tools and labour. The planners at the MAP were in the unpleasant position of having to compromise between the unrelenting demands of the Prime Minister that the bomber programme had to be met and the almost equally uncompromising realism of the engine firms, whose executives pointed out that a great deal of the increase of tool capacity was being absorbed in producing a constant output of engines whose performance and quality, and therefore mechanical complexity and cost in real terms, was steadily increasing.

The instability in the programmes, and in the output which was supposed to correspond to them, arose largely from the fact that accurate predictions could not be made of the date on which production could start and of the rate at which it would increase. Such predictions as were made were invariably optimistic by anything from six months to two years. Once a developed engine became established in production in one or more factories, the prediction of output became a relatively straightforward matter, but until this stage was reached an informed guess was the most that could be expected.

With the newer engines, however, this could not be done. The output of the newer marks of Merlin and Griffon in 1942, 1943 and 1944 was invariably below expectations and a source of disappointment to the Ministries, especially when their guesses had become invested with moral overtones. This applied particularly to the Merlin with two-stage two-speed overchargers and two-piece blocks. The first Merlin of this series, the Merlin 61, was such an outstanding success that the Air Ministry authorised an immediate production order before the type test had been completed. It was installed in a new mark of high-altitude Spitfire which was urgently required by Fighter Command early in 1942 to meet the challenge of the Focke-Wulf 190 fighter, a superb machine which completely outclassed the older mark of Spitfire. The development of the Merlin 60 series of engines had been given priority late in 1941 and in consequence work on the Griffon had suffered and this engine was not brought into production at Derby in any appreciable quantity until 1943. Even in this year only

396 were produced. This figure was raised to 1,257 in 1944. But the new mark of Merlin had such an improved performance that the Griffon, in its early stages, had a very small margin of performance to commend it. This again justified Hives's policy that the industry should develop known rather than unknown engines. A further argument in favour of this policy was the fact that the factories were also familiar with the production problems of the known engine and it was always easier to introduce even a substantial modification such as a two-speed supercharger to an engine already in production than to introduce a completely new engine such as the Griffon or Vulture.

The output of the group in 1942 nevertheless did not fall very far below expectations in so far as the grand total of engines was concerned, although there was a constant demand for the latest types, especially from Fighter Command. The Rolls-Royce factories produced 17,400 engines and with the output of Merlin XXs from the Ford factory this provided a total of 21,300. The peak output for all four factories during 1942 was achieved in October when over 2,000 engines were produced. The single-stage Merlin XX was the main engine manufactured during 1942 and Fords and Glasgow provided the majority of these. But towards the end of the year it became apparent that the output of Rolls-Royce factories could not be expected to increase very much beyond these figures. All three Rolls-Royce factories produced just under 6,000 complete engines, and though a considerable increase was expected from the Ford factory, this was to be obtained only if no change in mark was introduced.

During 1943 the production at the Rolls-Royce factories increased slightly to 18,800 while the production at Fords almost doubled, reaching a total of 6,900. But this again was largely explained by the fact that whereas the Ford factory confined itself to the Merlin XX series, both Derby and Crewe were faced with the problem of introducing two-stage Merlin production. The Derby factory was also producing the Griffon during 1943 and towards the end of the same year Crewe began to make preparations for its introduction. The production effort at Glasgow in 1942 and 1943 was in fact much greater than the figures for complete engines (5,750 and 6,576) reveal. In 1942 Rolls-Royce agreed to accept responsibility for the Packard Merlin engines which were beginning to arrive in England for installation in the Lancaster and other aircraft. The first batch of these engines, though they were excellent from all other points of view, required one important modification to the connecting rods which involved extensive dismantling and rebuilding. The engines also lacked a variety of installation fittings which through some oversight had not been ordered when the original order for the first 6,000 engines was placed. This deficiency was remedied in all subsequent orders, but in 1942 and 1943 the engines could not have been installed in British aircraft had Rolls-Royce not agreed to carry out the modifications and arranged for the manufacture of the supplementary items. The supplies of Packard engines in 1942 were not as great as the MAP had originally expected, but in 1943 no less than 5,261 Packard Merlins were rectified at Glasgow. The output of repaired engines at this factory was also substantial.

The maximum effort of the group was attained in 1944 when a total of 28,200 engines were produced, including 10,100 from the Ford factory. The actual quantitative totals from the three Rolls-Royce factories were lower by a few hundred engines in 1944 than in 1943 at each factory, but the production effort was much greater since the more complicated Merlins and the Griffon required a far larger number of machining-hours in their production than the simpler marks of engine. The comparative output of Derby is all the more impressive in view of the fact that in 1943 no less than fifteen marks of Merlin, ranging from the Merlin 20 to the Merlin 73, and seven marks of Griffon were produced at the Derby factory. In 1944 this had been reduced to eight marks of Merlin, though the number of marks of Griffon remained the same. The Crewe factory was also obliged to produce a large variety of engines (fifteen marks of Merlin in 1943), and in 1944 the Griffon was introduced at this factory as well. There had been hopes of a substantial supply of the two-stage engine from the United States as soon as the Packard Company had developed its production of this engine, but Packards did not prove any more capable than the parent organisation of changing rapidly from the production of the earlier to the later types. The production of two-stage engines was therefore started at Glasgow in 1944 as an insurance.

From a production point of view the problem would have been greatly simplified if the demand for the older marks of engines had declined as that for the newer marks increased. This never happened and the considerable lag was as much an indication of the remarkable rate of Merlin development as it was an indication of the reluctance of MAP officials to risk a shortage of any mark of engine. When 'maximum production' is looked upon as one of the main objectives in wartime, the mere quantitative totals appear at times to have a mesmerising effect and the intrinsic and ever-changing relationship between quantity and quality has frequently to be rediscovered. The process of rediscovery often seems to involve a considerable waste of resources. Thus towards the end of the war large surpluses of the earlier marks of Merlin began to accumulate and the apparatus of control did not prove as responsive as might have been expected by this time. There was no equivalent of the 'market' response to surplus or obsolescence. The output of two-stage engines and Griffons from Derby and Crewe would have been substantially greater in 1943 and 1944 had these factories not been obliged to carry the burden of producing simultaneously several other marks of Merlin to supplement the output of the other two factories. In many respects the very flexibility of the Derby factory in particular proved its own undoing from the quantity production point of view. This was especially the case when the RAF suddenly discovered that one of its aircraft flew better with a Merlin and asked for Merlins to be installed. At worst this required the production of a special engine (when the demand was for a particular type of performance); at best it required the modification of an existing mark to such an appreciable extent that the engine became virtually a new mark. The production of such an engine with its minor, but from a production point of view extremely important, peculiarities at one of the mass-production factories would have involved great dislocation of machines and methods, and consequently the work had to be undertaken by the two factories where flexible techniques had been maintained. The cost of this flexibility does not always seem to have been clearly appreciated at either the MAP or the Air Ministry. But when the need arose the superiority which it conferred on RAF fighters was very substantial.

During 1942 and 1943 there was a much greater measure of agreement between the management and the Ministries. From time to time the MAP continued to make extravagant demands in its programmes but under the influence of Sir Wilfrid Freeman, who returned to the MAP as Chief Executive in late 1942, a stronger sense of the limitations of statistics and of the practical significance of the programme was induced in MAP officials. On the question of engine development Hives had undoubtedly won, and proved, his point. As far as recipro-cating engines were concerned the Ministries did not again lose faith in the potentialities of the Merlin. The development of this remarkable engine continued into the Merlin 100 series which employed petrol-injection instead of the old type of carburation. The more hopeful production targets were not hit, especially in the later marks of engine, and at one stage in 1943 – one of the few occasions during the war on which it was necessary to do so – Spitfires were ferried with slave engines. This occurred while Hives was in America on a tour of the American aircraft industry and Sir Wilfrid Freeman asked the Chairman, Lord Herbert Scott, to use his personal influence to improve two-stage Merlin production. Lord Herbert Scott referred the matter to the Managing Director, who ordered a full investigation. This revealed that the firm could not altogether be blamed for what had happened.

In some respects, as Sidgreaves admitted to the Chairman, the firm had tied its own noose. 'I'm afraid', he said, 'that our enthusiasm and zeal to introduce new types has been greater than our real ability to do so. In other words we set ourselves too difficult a target because of our enthusiasm to give the R.A.F. the very best and latest engines at the earliest possible moment.' Sidgreaves considered that the firm had been too accommodating in accepting frequent changes of type in programmes from the MAP and that the Ministry had almost come to take production miracles for granted. He would not accept the charge of a general shortage since production in August had exceeded absorption by 600 engines and he considered that Sir Wilfrid Freeman was exaggerating when he stated that the deficiencies were having an adverse effect upon the whole aircraft programme. 'We know the position pretty well', he remarked, 'and can say that so far we have managed to keep the aircraft constructors all going fully with engines, with the possible exception of a small shortage of the particular type of two-stage variety used in the latest Mosquito.' In a memorandum on the subject Mr Swift (general manager of aircraft production) pointed out that the supply of tools, labour and materials had not been as great as promised and he also considered that a contributory cause was the waste of materials and labour in the production of the older marks of engine for which the demand from the aircraft constructors was steadily diminishing. The number of marks in production had increased steadily and a great effort had been put into the production of special engines which had been ordered in small quantities and which in one case were not even used. In October 1942 Hives had told the board that the MAP were unwise to expect a production of 22,500 engines in 1943, partly on account of the shortage of tools and labour but even more so because of the multiplicity of types. 'The time has arrived', he continued, 'when the M.A.P. have got to cut down the luxury articles in their programme. We know how much effort and capacity is tied up on projects which have a very doubtful value.' This warning was not heeded and the retarded evolution of the two-stage Merlin and Griffon engines was one of the principal consequences.

And in the end the war was won. It ended in Europe on what was called VE Day in May 1945 and in the Far East on VJ Day three months later in August. As we have seen in this book Rolls-Royce made a great, perhaps the greatest, contribution of any industrial company in the British Isles to the winning of that war. And one man, Ernest Hives, ran that company like no other could have done. There are many examples of his leadership and man-management qualities.

At the height of the war when he was responsible for running the Derby plant as well as supervising the Crewe and Glasgow factories, he also found time to deal with industrial problems on the shop floor. As ever there was a left-wing element among the shop stewards and these had used a Glasgow Communist to create unrest. In fact, the shop stewards sent a resolution for an immediate general election with foreign policy as the issue. Hives commented: 'You will see that we have people here who are ambitious enough not only to dictate how we shall run the factory, but also how the country should be run.' He tackled industrial problems directly, meeting the shop stewards over the issue of the closed shop and telling them that he was not prepared to discuss anything with them that was in the nature of a threat. He was determined to protect old servants of the company that might be at risk. He also introduced visits by wives and girlfriends of the employees to look around the factory and have tea before they went home. It proved very popular, with 70 per cent of the men asking for invitations. Hives thought that when the wives saw present working conditions the men would get less sympathy when they suggested striking.

Ever mindful of his workforce, Hives found time to write to Beaverbrook urging that operational pilots should be sent to the Rolls-Royce factories, not only to talk to the workforce but to see at first hand the efforts that were being made on their behalf, and he suggested that Wing Commander Helmore should be put in charge of this special publicity for the Rolls-Royce factories.

As we have seen, Hives, with his straightforward, common-sense approach, generated trust that persuaded even civil servants and Government ministers to throw their usual caution to the winds. Remember Beaverbrook's letter to him just after the Dunkirk retreat in June 1940:

I appoint you Chairman of a Committee of One required to deal with

Rolls-Royce properties in the case of enemy attack. You have complete authority and discretion in the organisation of R.R. output on such terms and conditions as you desire. Your authority will also extend to all sub-contractors of Rolls-Royce whose works may be subjected to enemy attack.

We have also seen that he was fearless in standing up to those whose bureaucratic tendencies hindered Rolls-Royce's efforts to produce as many engines as possible:

Please do not refer me to another government department or point out that there is a shortage of building materials. You would be surprised if you knew all the shortages that we have to contend with and overcome.

If you look at the map you will find that Hitler has penetrated 1,000 miles into Russia up to the present while we have been waiting for the M.A.P. to make up their minds on Vulture repairs.

Fortunately for Hives, Beaverbrook recognised in him a man who got things done so he was prepared to tolerate Hives at his most mischievous as when he replied to a telegram from a Ministry official who signed himself 'DAPF6':

We have started a form-filling-in department for the Ministry of Labour, the Ministry of Health and the M.A.P. but Mr D.A.P.F.6 we propose to ignore.

Nor was Hives afraid to stand up to his chairman. As we saw, he wrote to Managing Director Sidgreaves when Sir Herbert Scott had suggested that Rolls-Royce do all they could to prevent Napier going into full production of the Sabre:

I thought it had been accepted that the only thing that mattered was to win the war and that the question of commercial prestige was to be forgotten in the present struggle.

From the very beginning, Henry Royce had recognised in Hives a man who 'had a good ear for an engine allied to an acute diagnostic mind'.

On 11 January 1949, Marshal of the Royal Air Force Lord Tedder unveiled a stained-glass window in the Front Hall of the Rolls-Royce factory in Nightingale Road, Derby. It was dedicated 'To the pilots of the Royal Air Force who, in the Battle of Britain, turned the work of our hands into the salvation of our country.'

Sir Archibald Sinclair, who had been Secretary of State for War from 1940 to 1945, said at the opening ceremony:

I remember one night being called out of a meeting of the Defence Committee to be told that German bombers were approaching and that the radio beam which directed them was laid on a line which passed near Derby. We would far rather have heard that the beam was laid on Downing Street or that parachutists were dropping in St James's Park. For all our fighters in the Battle of Britain were powered by Rolls-Royce Merlin engines, and at that time nearly all came from those Derby works – although Crewe was just beginning to get into its stride. Production of Merlins was not much over 2,000 in 1939. There were many customers besides Fighter Command. Our losses, too, in the battle were heavy. So Rolls-Royce stepped up production from just over 2,000 to 7,000 in 1940. What does this prodigious achievement represent in human effort? Give praise to the Ministry of Aircraft Production, glowing with energy under the titanic leadership of Lord Beaverbrook – the most ruthless breaker of bottle-necks in history. He made the plant and tools and raw materials flow to our aircraft and engine factories just in time. He gave Rolls-Royce the tools, and what a job of research, design, production and repair the management and workers did! There was one frequent visitor from Rolls-Royce to the Ministry of Aircraft Production and to the Commands of the RAF. He was in the confidence of the Air Staff, he was foremost among the many representatives of Rolls-Royce who kept in close and constant touch with the RAF and its requirements, and he seemed to us to personify the ceaseless, thrusting, imaginative energy, purpose and will to a victory which animated Rolls-Royce – and that was Mr Ernest

Walter Hives. Long may he be spared to fertilise by his genius, and inspire by his example, the work of your hands and brains!

Hives, modest and to-the-point, as always, said, 'We workers at Rolls-Royce like to consider ourselves part of the RAF. We recognise that our efforts were more congenial and we were not called upon to display the courage and suffer the hardships and the sacrifices of the fighter pilots. Nevertheless, we hope we shall not be considered impertinent if we insist on our claims that we were a part of the RAF in the battle. We would like it to be thought', he added, 'that where the inscription on the window reads "our hands", this covers not only the workers in the Rolls-Royce factories, but all those on the industrial side who made their contribution.' It should not be forgotten that Hives lost a son himself, shot down over France.

As we have seen, Hives could be blunt and did not suffer fools gladly. He could be particularly hard on civil servants – he no doubt admired people who created or made something rather than those who organised affairs – but, if he admired someone, civil servant or not, he worked with them to the utmost of his ability. One such was Wilfrid Freeman who, in turn, admired and respected him. This is what Anthony Furse wrote of the relationship in his biography of Freeman:

Ernest Hives, the General Manager of Rolls-Royce, was one of the very few people Freeman admired without reservations. Helped by the full backing of his Board, Hives had the perception to concentrate most of the formidable resources of Rolls-Royce on two engines, which greatly simplified the expansion of production, when three new factories in Britain and one in America (making Packard Merlins) came into production.

Although his delivery forecasts sometimes slipped, Freeman trusted Hives as he had trusted Tedder in 1938–1940, and was in turn greatly respected by Hives. Even when Freeman was VCAS, they wrote to each other frequently and frankly, and met occasionally, although it was 'against the rules', and Freeman was deeply impressed by – and immensely grateful for – the speed with which Rolls-Royce brought into production the regular improvements in engine power which culminated in the two-stage Merlin and Griffon engines. Merlins powered the Mosquito and 95 per cent of the Lancasters, and, apart from the period of about nine months before deliveries of Spitfire IXs began, when the new German FW 190 was superior to the Spitfire Vs, successive Rolls-Royce piston engines in the various marks of Spitfire, gave them a qualitative edge over the German fighters throughout the war.

Major Bulman, who also worked closely with Hives throughout the 1930s and during the war, wrote in his memoirs:

Beyond doubt the man mainly responsible for the achievements of the firm, perpetuating the spirit of Royce himself (who died in 1933, never returning to Derby after 1914), was Ernest Hives. He had been apprenticed to the firm's repair depot in London in 1906, went on to Derby to become foreman of the experimental engine machine shop – as when I first remember him around 1919, and was to become General Manager throughout the second war, a Companion of Honour (through his 'Artistry in Engine Design'), Chairman and a Baron. But he was always the same, inimitable and fundamentally simple 'Hs', as he was always known throughout the works under that distinctive Rolls habit of designating everybody by their own initials or something similar (he was also known as 'the Boss' and 'Uncle Ernie'). Thereby all communication verbal or written was accomplished with no differentiation or embarrassment of relative rank.

BIBLIOGRAPHY OF BOOKS CONSULTED

Banks, F. Rodwell, *I Kept no Diary*, Airlife, 1978

Barker, Ralph, *The Schneider Trophy Races*, Chatto & Windus/ Random House UK, 1971

Birch, David, *Rolls-Royce and the Mustang*, Rolls-Royce Heritage Trust (Historical Series Vol. 9), 1987

Bishop, Edward, *Hurricane*, Airlife, 1986

Bowyer, Chaz, *History of the RAF*, Hamlyn, 1985

Bowyer, Michael, *The Spitfire 50 Years On*, Patrick Stephens, 1986

Clarke, Peter, *Hope, Glory, Britain 1900–1990*, Penguin, 1996

Deighton, Len, *Battle of Britain*, Jonathan Cape, 1980

Dibbs, John and Holmes, Tony, *Hurricane – a Fighter Legend*, Osprey/Aerospace, 1995

Douglas, Sholto, *Years of Command*, Collins, 1966

Fedden, Sir Roy, *Britain's Air Survival – an Appraisement and Strategy for Success*, Cassell & Co. Ltd., 1957

Gilbert, Martin, *A History of the Twentieth Century, Volume One: 1900–1933*, HarperCollins, 1997

Gilbert, Martin, *A History of the Twentieth Century, Volume Two: 1933–1951*, HarperCollins, 1998

Griffiths, Harry, *Testing Times – Memories of a Spitfire Boffin*, United Writers Publications, 1992

Gunston, Bill, *Rolls-Royce, Aero Engines*, Patrick Stephens, 1989

Harker, R.W., *Rolls-Royce from the Wings*, Oxford Illustrated Press, 1976

Harker, R.W., *The Engines Were Rolls-Royce*, Collier Macmillan, 1980

Harvey-Bailey, Alec, *Rolls-Royce – Hives, the Quiet Tiger*, Sir Henry Royce Memorial Foundation (Historical Series Vol. 7), 1986

Harvey-Bailey, Alec, *Rolls-Royce – Hives' Turbulent Barons*, Sir Henry Royce Memorial Foundation (Historical Series Vol. 20), 1993

Harvey-Bailey, Alec, *The Merlin in Perspective – the Combat Years*, Rolls-Royce Heritage Trust (Historical Series Vol. 2, 4th edition), 1995

Henshaw, Alex, *Sigh for Merlin*, John Murray, 1979

Hooker, Sir Stanley, *Not much of an Engineer*, Airlife, 1984

James, Derek N., *Schneider Trophy Aircraft 1913–31*, Bodley Head, 1981

Kaplan, Philip and Collier, Richard, *The Few*, Blandford Press, 1989

Lacey, Robert, *Ford, the Men and the Machine*, Heinemann, 1986

Miller, William J., *Memoirs*, private publication, 1980s

Mitchell, Gordon, *R.J. Mitchell, Schooldays to Spitfire*, Gordon Mitchell, 1986

Mondey, David, *The Schneider Trophy*, Robert Hale, 1975

Nockolds, Harold, *The Magic of a Name*, G.T. Foulis, 1959

Penrose, Harald, *British Aviation – the Adventuring Years 1920–39*, Putnam, 1963

Penrose, Harald, *British Aviation – the Great War and Armistice*, Putnam, 1969

Penrose, Harald, *British Aviation – Widening Horizons, 1930–34*, HMSO, 1979

Penrose, Harald, *British Aviation – the Ominous Skies 1935–39*, HMSO, 1980

Penrose, Harald, *Adventure with Fate*, Airlife, 1984

Price, Alfred, *The Spitfire Story*, Arms & Armour Press/Cassell, 1992

Quill, Jeffrey K., OBE, *Spitfire, A Test Pilot's Story*, John Murray, 1983

Quill, Jeffrey K., OBE, *The Birth of a Legend*, Quiller Press, 1986

Richie, Sebastian, *Industry and Air Power – the Expansion of British Aircraft Production, 1935–1941*, Frank Cass, 1997

Robertson, Bruce, *Spitfire – the Story of a Famous Fighter*, Harleyford Publications, 1973

Rubbra, A.A., *Rolls-Royce Piston Aero Engines – a Designer Remembers*, Rolls-Royce Heritage Trust, 1990

Sarkar, Dilip, *Invisible Thread: Spitfire's Tale*, Ramrod Publications, 1992

Schlaiffer, Robert and Heron, S.D., *Development of Aircraft Engines and Development of Aviation Fuels*, Harvard Business School, 1950

Shacklady, Edward and Morgan, Eric B., *Spitfire – the History*, Key Publishing Company, 1987

Sims, Charles, *Royal Air Force, The First 50 Years*, Adam & Charles Black Ltd., 1968

Stait, Bruce, *Rotol, the History of an Airscrew Company, 1937–1960*, Alan Sutton, 1990

Stewart, Adrian, *Hurricane*, William Kimber & Co. Ltd., 1982

Thorne, A., *Lancaster at War*, I. Allan, 1990

Tuffen, H.J. and Tagg, A.E., *The Hawker Hurricane, Design, Development and Production*, Royal Aeronautical Society, Historical Group, 1988

Whitney, Daniel D., *Vees for Victory! The Story of the Allison V-1710, 1929–1948*, Schiffer Military History, 1998

INDEX